Chemistry revision? CGP has the solution...

No doubt about it, GCSE Chemistry is a tough subject. Luckily, this CGP book has everything you'll need, from facts and theory to practical skills — and what's more, there are practice questions on each page to help you sharpen up your exam skills.

How to access your free Online Edition

This book includes a free Online Edition to read on your PC, Mac or tablet. To access it, just go to **cgpbooks.co.uk/extras** and enter this code...

1783 3613 9490 1096

By the way, this code only works for one person. If somebody else has used this book before you, they might have already claimed the Online Edition.

CGP — still the best! ☺

Our sole aim here at CGP is to produce the highest quality books — carefully written, immaculately presented and dangerously close to being funny.

Then we work our socks off to get them out to you — at the cheapest possible prices.

Contents

Published by CGP.
From original material by Richard Parsons.

Editors: Mary Falkner, Emily Forsberg, Paul Jordin and Sophie Scott
Contributor: Paddy Gannon

ISBN: 978 1 78294 572 7

With thanks to Emily Howe and Jamie Sinclair for the proofreading.

With thanks to Ana Pungartnik for the copyright research.

Contains public sector information published by the Health and Safety Executive and licensed under the Open Government Licence. http://www.nationalarchives.gov.uk/doc/open-government-licence/version/3/.

Graph to show trend in Atmospheric CO_2 Concentration and global temperature on page 93 based on data by EPICA community members 2004 and Siegenthaler et al 2005.

Printed by Elanders Ltd, Newcastle upon Tyne.
Clipart from Corel®
Illustrations by: Sandy Gardner Artist, email sandy@sandygardner.co.uk

The Scientific Method

This section isn't about how to 'do' science — but it does show you the way most scientists work.

Scientists Come Up With Hypotheses — Then Test Them

1) Scientists try to explain things. They start by observing something they don't understand.

2) They then come up with a hypothesis — a possible explanation for what they've observed.

3) The next step is to test whether the hypothesis might be right or not. This involves making a prediction based on the hypothesis and testing it by gathering evidence (i.e. data) from investigations. If evidence from experiments backs up a prediction, you're a step closer to figuring out if the hypothesis is true.

About 100 years ago, scientists hypothesised that atoms looked like this.

Several Scientists Will Test a Hypothesis

1) Normally, scientists share their findings in peer-reviewed journals, or at conferences.

2) Peer-review is where other scientists check results and scientific explanations to make sure they're 'scientific' (e.g. that experiments have been done in a sensible way) before they're published. It helps to detect false claims, but it doesn't mean that findings are correct — just that they're not wrong in any obvious way.

3) Once other scientists have found out about a hypothesis, they'll start basing their own predictions on it and carry out their own experiments. They'll also try to reproduce the original experiments to check the results — and if all the experiments in the world back up the hypothesis, then scientists start to think the hypothesis is true.

4) However, if a scientist does an experiment that doesn't fit with the hypothesis (and other scientists can reproduce the results) then the hypothesis may need to be modified or scrapped altogether.

After more evidence was gathered, scientists changed their hypothesis to this.

If All the Evidence Supports a Hypothesis, It's Accepted — For Now

1) Accepted hypotheses are often referred to as theories. Our currently accepted theories are the ones that have survived this 'trial by evidence' — they've been tested many times over the years and survived.

2) However, theories never become totally indisputable fact. If new evidence comes along that can't be explained using the existing theory, then the hypothesising and testing is likely to start all over again.

Now we think it's more like this.

Theories Can Involve Different Types of Models

1) A representational model is a simplified description or picture of what's going on in real life. Like all models, it can be used to explain observations and make predictions. E.g. the Bohr model of an atom is a simplified way of showing the arrangement of electrons in an atom (see p.15). It can be used to explain trends down groups in the periodic table.

Scientists test models by carrying out experiments to check that the predictions made by the model happen as expected.

2) Computational models use computers to make simulations of complex real-life processes, such as climate change. They're used when there are a lot of different variables (factors that change) to consider, and because you can easily change their design to take into account new data.

3) All models have limitations on what they can explain or predict. E.g. ball and stick models (a type of spatial model) can be used to show how ions are arranged in an ionic compound. One of their limitations is that they don't show the relative sizes of the ions (see p.22).

I'm off to the zoo to test my hippo-thesis...

The scientific method has developed over time, and many people have helped to develop it. From Aristotle to modern day scientists, lots of people have contributed. And many more are likely to contribute in the future.

Communication & Issues Created by Science

Scientific developments can be great, but they can sometimes <u>raise more questions</u> than they answer...

It's Important to Communicate Scientific Discoveries to the General Public

Some scientific discoveries show that people should <u>change their habits</u>, or they might provide ideas that could be <u>developed</u> into new <u>technology</u>. So scientists need to <u>tell the world</u> about their discoveries.

> Technologies are being developed that make use of <u>fullerenes</u> (see p.24). These include <u>drug delivery systems</u> for use in medicine. Information about these systems needs to be communicated to <u>doctors</u> so they can <u>make use</u> of them, and to <u>patients</u>, so they can make <u>informed decisions</u> about their <u>treatment</u>.

Scientific Evidence can be Presented in a Biased Way

1) Reports about scientific discoveries in the <u>media</u> (e.g. newspapers or television) <u>aren't</u> peer-reviewed.

2) This means that, even though news stories are often <u>based</u> on data that has been peer-reviewed, the data might be <u>presented</u> in a way that is <u>over-simplified</u> or <u>inaccurate</u>, making it open to <u>misinterpretation</u>.

3) People who want to make a point can sometimes <u>present data</u> in a <u>biased way</u>. (Sometimes <u>without knowing</u> they're doing it.) For example, a scientist might overemphasise a relationship in the data, or a newspaper article might describe details of data <u>supporting</u> an idea without giving any evidence <u>against</u> it.

Scientific Developments are Great, but they can Raise Issues

Scientific <u>knowledge is increased</u> by doing experiments. And this knowledge leads to <u>scientific developments</u>, e.g. new technologies or new advice. These developments can create <u>issues</u> though. For example:

<u>Economic issues:</u> Society <u>can't</u> always <u>afford</u> to do things scientists recommend (e.g. investing in alternative energy sources) without <u>cutting back elsewhere</u>.

<u>Personal issues:</u> Some decisions will affect <u>individuals</u>. For example, someone might support <u>alternative energy</u>, but object if a <u>wind farm</u> was built next to their house.

<u>Social issues:</u> Decisions based on scientific evidence affect <u>people</u> — e.g. should fossil fuels be taxed more highly? <u>Would the effect on people's lifestyles be acceptable?</u>

<u>Environmental issues:</u> <u>Human activity</u> often affects the <u>natural environment</u>. For example, building a <u>dam</u> to produce electricity will change the <u>local habitat</u> so some species might be displaced. But it will also reduce our need for <u>fossil fuels</u>, so will help to reduce <u>climate change</u>.

Science Can't Answer Every Question — Especially Ethical Ones

1) We don't <u>understand everything</u>. We're always finding out <u>more</u>, but we'll never know <u>all</u> the answers.

2) In order to answer scientific questions, scientists need <u>data</u> to provide <u>evidence</u> for their hypotheses.

3) Some questions can't be answered <u>yet</u> because the data <u>can't</u> currently be <u>collected</u>, or because there's <u>not enough</u> data to <u>support</u> a theory.

4) <u>Eventually</u>, as we get <u>more evidence</u>, we'll answer some of the questions that <u>currently</u> can't be answered, e.g. what the impact of global warming on sea levels will be. But there will always be the "<u>Should we be doing this at all?</u>"-type questions that experiments <u>can't</u> help us to answer...

> Think about <u>new drugs which can be taken to boost your 'brain power'</u>.
>
> * Some people think they're <u>good</u> as they could improve concentration or memory. New drugs could let people think in ways beyond the powers of normal brains.
> * Other people say they're <u>bad</u> — they could give you an <u>unfair advantage</u> in exams. And people might be <u>pressured</u> into taking them so that they could work more <u>effectively</u>, and for <u>longer hours</u>.

Tea to milk or milk to tea? — Totally unanswerable by science...

Science can't tell you whether or not you should do something. That's for you and society to decide. But there are tons of questions science might be able to answer, like where life came from and where my superhero socks are.

Risk

By reading this page you are agreeing to the <u>risk</u> of a paper cut or severe drowsiness...

Nothing is Completely Risk-Free

1) A <u>hazard</u> is something that could <u>potentially cause harm</u>.

2) All hazards have a <u>risk</u> attached to them — this is the <u>chance</u> that the hazard will cause harm.

3) The risks of some things seem pretty <u>obvious</u>, or we've known about them for a while, like the risk of causing <u>acid rain</u> by polluting the atmosphere, or of having a <u>car accident</u> when you're travelling in a car.

4) <u>New technology</u> arising from <u>scientific advances</u> can bring <u>new risks</u>, e.g. scientists are unsure whether <u>nanoparticles</u> that are being used in cosmetics and suncream might be harming the cells in our bodies. These risks need to be considered <u>alongside</u> the <u>benefits</u> of the technology, e.g. improved sun protection.

5) You can estimate the <u>size</u> of a risk based on <u>how many times</u> something happens in a big sample (e.g. 100 000 people) over a given <u>period</u> (e.g. a year). For example, you could assess the risk of a driver crashing by recording how many people in a group of 100 000 drivers crashed their cars over a year.

6) To make <u>decisions</u> about activities that involve <u>hazards</u>, we need to take into account the <u>chance</u> of the hazard causing harm, and how <u>serious</u> the <u>consequences</u> would be if it did. If an activity involves a hazard that's <u>very likely</u> to cause harm, with <u>serious consequences</u> if it does, it's considered <u>high risk</u>.

People Make Their Own Decisions About Risk

1) Not all risks have the same <u>consequences</u>, e.g. if you chop veg with a sharp knife you risk cutting your finger, but if you go scuba-diving you risk death. You're much <u>more likely</u> to cut your finger during half an hour of <u>chopping</u> than to die during half an hour of <u>scuba-diving</u>. But most people are happier to accept a higher <u>probability</u> of an accident if the <u>consequences</u> are <u>short-lived</u> and fairly <u>minor</u>.

2) People tend to be more willing to accept a risk if they <u>choose</u> to do something (e.g. go scuba diving), compared to having the risk <u>imposed</u> on them (e.g. having a nuclear power station built next door).

3) People's <u>perception</u> of risk (how risky they <u>think</u> something is) isn't always <u>accurate</u>. They tend to view <u>familiar</u> activities as <u>low-risk</u> and <u>unfamiliar</u> activities as <u>high-risk</u> — even if that's not the case. For example, cycling on roads is often <u>high-risk</u>, but many people are happy to do it because it's a <u>familiar</u> activity. Air travel is actually pretty <u>safe</u>, but a lot of people perceive it as <u>high-risk</u>.

4) People may <u>over-estimate</u> the risk of things with <u>long-term</u> or <u>invisible</u> effects, e.g. ionising radiation.

Investigations Can be Hazardous

1) Hazards from science experiments might include:

- <u>Microorganisms</u>, e.g. some bacteria can make you ill.
- <u>Chemicals</u>, e.g. sulfuric acid can burn your skin and alcohols catch fire easily.
- <u>Fire</u>, e.g. an unattended Bunsen burner is a fire hazard.
- <u>Electricity</u>, e.g. faulty electrical equipment could give you a shock.

Hmm... Where did my bacteria sample go?

2) Part of planning an investigation is making sure that it's <u>safe</u>.

3) You should always make sure that you <u>identify</u> all the hazards that you might encounter. Then you should think of ways of <u>reducing the risks</u> from the hazards you've identified. For example:

- If you're working with <u>sulfuric acid</u>, always wear gloves and safety goggles. This will reduce the risk of the acid coming into contact with your skin and eyes.
- If you're using a <u>Bunsen burner</u>, stand it on a heat proof mat. This will reduce the risk of starting a fire.

> You can find out about potential hazards by looking in textbooks, doing some internet research, or asking your teacher.

Not revising — an unacceptable exam hazard...

The world's a dangerous place, but if you can recognise hazards, decide how to reduce their risks, and be happy to accept some risks, you can still have fun. Just maybe don't go skydiving with a great white shark on Friday 13th.

Designing Investigations

Dig out your lab coat and dust down your badly-scratched safety goggles... it's <u>investigation time</u>.

Investigations Produce Evidence to Support or Disprove a Hypothesis

1) Scientists <u>observe</u> things and come up with <u>hypotheses</u> to explain them (see p.2).
   You need to be able to do the same. For example:

   > <u>Observation</u>: People have big feet and spots. <u>Hypothesis</u>: Having big feet causes spots.

2) To <u>determine</u> whether or not a hypothesis is <u>right</u>, you need to do an <u>investigation</u> to gather evidence. To do this, you need to use your hypothesis to make a <u>prediction</u> — something you think <u>will happen</u> that you can test. E.g. people who have bigger feet will have more spots.

3) Investigations are used to see if there are <u>patterns</u> or <u>relationships</u> between <u>two variables</u>, e.g. to see if there's a pattern or relationship between the variables 'number of spots' and 'size of feet'.

Evidence Needs to be Repeatable, Reproducible and Valid

1) <u>Repeatable</u> means that if the <u>same person</u> does an experiment again using the <u>same methods</u> and equipment, they'll get <u>similar results</u>.

2) <u>Reproducible</u> means that if <u>someone else</u> does the experiment, or a <u>different</u> method or piece of equipment is used, the results will still be <u>similar</u>.

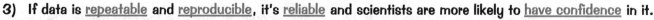
Investigations include experiments and studies.

3) If data is <u>repeatable</u> and <u>reproducible</u>, it's <u>reliable</u> and scientists are more likely to <u>have confidence</u> in it.

4) <u>Valid results</u> are both repeatable and reproducible AND they <u>answer the original question</u>. They come from experiments that were designed to be a <u>FAIR TEST</u>...

To Make an Investigation a Fair Test You Have to Control the Variables

1) In a lab experiment you usually <u>change one variable</u> and <u>measure</u> how it affects <u>another variable</u>.

2) To make it a fair test, <u>everything else</u> that could affect the results should <u>stay the same</u> — otherwise you can't tell if the thing you're changing is causing the results or not.

3) The variable you <u>CHANGE</u> is called the <u>INDEPENDENT</u> variable.

4) The variable you <u>MEASURE</u> when you change the independent variable is the <u>DEPENDENT</u> variable.

5) The variables that you <u>KEEP THE SAME</u> are called <u>CONTROL</u> variables.

   > You could find how <u>temperature</u> affects <u>reaction rate</u> by measuring the <u>volume of gas</u> formed over time. The <u>independent variable</u> is the <u>temperature</u>. The <u>dependent variable</u> is the <u>volume of gas</u> produced. <u>Control variables</u> include the <u>concentration</u> and <u>amounts</u> of reactants, the <u>time period</u> you measure, etc.

6) Because you can't always control all the variables, you often need to use a <u>control experiment</u>. This is an experiment that's kept under the <u>same conditions</u> as the rest of the investigation, but <u>doesn't</u> have anything <u>done</u> to it. This is so that you can see what happens when you don't change anything at all.

The Bigger the Sample Size the Better

1) Data based on <u>small samples</u> isn't as good as data based on large samples. A sample should <u>represent</u> the <u>whole population</u> (i.e. it should share as many of the characteristics in the population as possible) — a small sample can't do that as well. It's also harder to spot <u>anomalies</u> if your sample size is too small.

2) The <u>bigger</u> the sample size the <u>better</u>, but scientists have to be <u>realistic</u> when choosing how big. For example, if you were studying the effects of a chemical used to sterilise water on the people drinking it, it'd be great to study <u>everyone</u> who was drinking the water (a huge sample), but it'd take ages and cost a bomb. It's more realistic to study a thousand people, with a mixture of ages, gender, and race.

This is no high street survey — it's a designer investigation...

Not only do you need to be able to plan your own investigations, you should also be able to look at someone else's plan and decide whether or not it needs improving. Those examiners aren't half demanding.

Collecting Data

You've designed the perfect investigation — now it's time to get your hands mucky and collect some data.

Your Data Should be Repeatable, Reproducible, Accurate and Precise

1) To check repeatability you need to repeat the readings and check that the results are similar. You need to repeat each reading at least three times.

2) To make sure your results are reproducible you can cross check them by taking a second set of readings with another instrument (or a different observer).

3) Your data also needs to be ACCURATE. Really accurate results are those that are really close to the true answer. The accuracy of your results usually depends on your method — you need to make sure you're measuring the right thing and that you don't miss anything that should be included in the measurements. E.g. estimating the amount of gas released from a reaction by counting the bubbles isn't very accurate because you might miss some of the bubbles and they might have different volumes. It's more accurate to measure the volume of gas released using a gas syringe (see p.109).

4) Your data also needs to be PRECISE. Precise results are ones where the data is all really close to the mean (average) of your repeated results (i.e. not spread out).

Bess's result was a curate.

Repeat	Data set 1	Data set 2
1	12	11
2	14	17
3	13	14
Mean	13	14

Data set 1 is more precise than data set 2.

Your Equipment has to be Right for the Job

1) The measuring equipment you use has to be sensitive enough to measure the changes you're looking for. For example, if you need to measure changes of 1 cm³, you need to use a measuring cylinder or burette that can measure in 1 cm³ steps — it'd be no good trying with one that only measures 10 cm³ steps.

2) The smallest change a measuring instrument can detect is called its RESOLUTION. E.g. some mass balances have a resolution of 1 g, some have a resolution of 0.1 g, and some are even more sensitive.

3) Also, equipment needs to be calibrated by measuring a known value. If there's a difference between the measured and known value, you can use this to correct the inaccuracy of the equipment.

You Need to Look out for Errors and Anomalous Results

1) The results of your experiment will always vary a bit because of RANDOM ERRORS — unpredictable differences caused by things like human errors in measuring. The errors when you make a reading from a burette are random. You have to estimate or round the level when it's between two marks — so sometimes your figure will be a bit above the real one, and sometimes it will be a bit below.

2) You can reduce the effect of random errors by taking repeat readings and finding the mean. This will make your results more precise.

3) If a measurement is wrong by the same amount every time, it's called a SYSTEMATIC ERROR. For example, if you measured from the very end of your ruler instead of from the 0 cm mark every time, all your measurements would be a bit small. Repeating the experiment in the exact same way and calculating a mean won't correct a systematic error.

If there's no systematic error, then doing repeats and calculating a mean can make your results more accurate.

4) Just to make things more complicated, if a systematic error is caused by using equipment that isn't zeroed properly, it's called a ZERO ERROR. For example, if a mass balance always reads 1 gram before you put anything on it, all your measurements will be 1 gram too heavy.

5) You can compensate for some systematic errors if you know about them though, e.g. if your mass balance always reads 1 gram before you put anything on it you can subtract 1 gram from all your results.

6) Sometimes you get a result that doesn't fit in with the rest at all. This is called an ANOMALOUS RESULT. You should investigate it and try to work out what happened. If you can work out what happened (e.g. you measured something totally wrong) you can ignore it when processing your results.

Watch what you say to that mass balance — it's very sensitive...

Weirdly, data can be really precise but not very accurate. For example, a fancy piece of lab equipment might give results that are really precise, but if it's not been calibrated properly those results won't be accurate.

Processing and Presenting Data

Processing your data means doing some <u>calculations</u> with it to make it <u>more useful</u>. Once you've done that, you can present your results in a nice <u>chart</u> or <u>graph</u> to help you <u>spot any patterns</u> in your data.

Data Needs to be Organised

1) Tables are dead useful for <u>organising data</u>.

2) When you draw a table, <u>use a ruler</u> and make sure <u>each column</u> has a <u>heading</u> (including the <u>units</u>).

You Might Have to Process Your Data

1) When you've done repeats of an experiment, you should always calculate the <u>mean</u> (average). To do this <u>add together</u> all the data values and <u>divide</u> by the total number of values in the sample.

2) You might also need to calculate the <u>range</u> (how spread out the data is). To do this find the <u>largest</u> number and <u>subtract</u> the <u>smallest</u> number from it.

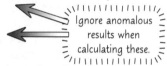 Ignore anomalous results when calculating these.

3) The <u>mode</u> is the <u>most common</u> result in your data set.

4) The <u>median</u> is the 'middle' value. You find it by arranging all your data in <u>numerical order</u>, and then seeing which value's in the middle. If there's two, you take the <u>mean</u> of them.

EXAMPLE: The results of an experiment to find the volume of gas produced in an enzyme-controlled reaction are shown below. Calculate the mean volume and the range.

Repeat 1 (cm³)	Repeat 2 (cm³)	Repeat 3 (cm³)	Mean (cm³)	Range (cm³)
28	37	32	(28 + 37 + 32) ÷ 3 = 32	37 − 28 = 9

Round to the Lowest Number of Significant Figures

The <u>first significant figure</u> of a number is the first digit that's <u>not zero</u>. The second and third significant figures come <u>straight after</u> (even if they're zeros). You should be aware of significant figures in calculations.

1) In <u>any</u> calculation, you should round the answer to the <u>lowest number of significant figures</u> (s.f.) given.

2) Remember to write down <u>how many</u> significant figures you've rounded to after your answer.

3) If your calculation has multiple steps, <u>only</u> round the <u>final</u> answer, or it won't be as accurate.

EXAMPLE: The mass of a solid is 0.24 g and its volume is 0.715 cm³. Calculate the density of the solid.

Density = 0.24 g ÷ 0.715 cm³ = 0.33566... = 0.34 g/cm³ (2 s.f.) — Final answer should be rounded to 2 s.f.

2 s.f.   3 s.f.

Bar Charts can be Used to Show Different Types of Data

Bar charts can be used to display:

1) <u>Categoric</u> data (comes in distinct categories, e.g. flower colour, blood group).

2) <u>Discrete</u> data (the data can be counted in chunks, where there's no in-between value, e.g. number of bacteria is discrete because you can't have half a bacterium).

3) <u>Continuous</u> data (numerical data that can have any value in a range, e.g. length or temperature).

There are some <u>golden rules</u> you need to follow for <u>drawing</u> bar charts:

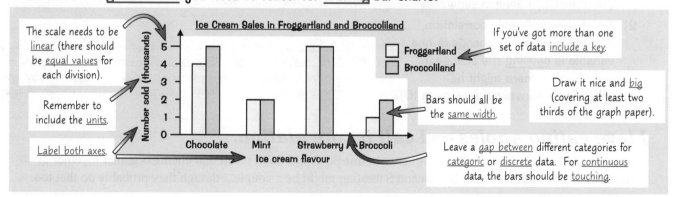

The scale needs to be <u>linear</u> (there should be <u>equal values</u> for each division).

Remember to include the <u>units</u>.

<u>Label both axes</u>.

If you've got more than one set of data <u>include a key</u>.

Draw it nice and <u>big</u> (covering at least two thirds of the graph paper).

Bars should all be the <u>same width</u>.

Leave a <u>gap between</u> different categories for <u>categoric</u> or <u>discrete</u> data. For <u>continuous</u> data, the bars should be <u>touching</u>.

Graphs Can be Used to Plot Continuous Data

If both variables are <u>continuous</u> you should use a <u>graph</u> to display the data.

Here are the rules for plotting points on a graph:

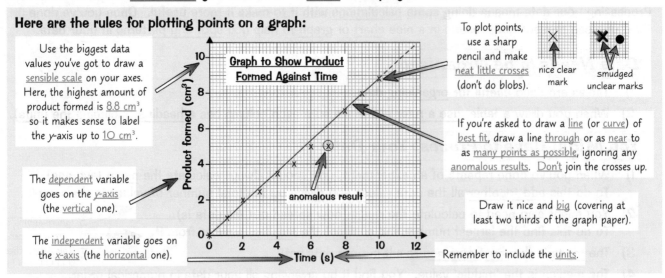

Use the biggest data values you've got to draw a <u>sensible scale</u> on your axes. Here, the highest amount of product formed is <u>8.8 cm³</u>, so it makes sense to label the y-axis up to <u>10 cm³</u>.

The <u>dependent</u> variable goes on the <u>y-axis</u> (the <u>vertical</u> one).

The <u>independent</u> variable goes on the <u>x-axis</u> (the <u>horizontal</u> one).

To plot points, use a sharp pencil and make <u>neat little crosses</u> (don't do blobs). nice clear mark / smudged unclear marks

If you're asked to draw a <u>line</u> (or <u>curve</u>) of <u>best fit</u>, draw a line <u>through</u> or as <u>near</u> to as <u>many points as possible</u>, ignoring any <u>anomalous results</u>. <u>Don't</u> join the crosses up.

Draw it nice and <u>big</u> (covering at least two thirds of the graph paper).

Remember to include the <u>units</u>.

Graphs Can Give You a Lot of Information About Your Data

1) The <u>gradient</u> (slope) of a graph tells you how quickly the <u>dependent variable</u> changes if you change the <u>independent variable</u>.

$$\text{gradient} = \frac{\text{change in } y}{\text{change in } x}$$

This <u>graph</u> shows the <u>volume of gas</u> produced in a reaction against <u>time</u>. The graph is <u>linear</u> (it's a straight line graph), so you can simply calculate the <u>gradient</u> of the line to find out the <u>rate of reaction</u>.

1) To calculate the gradient, pick <u>two points</u> on the line that are easy to read and a <u>good distance</u> apart.

2) <u>Draw a line down</u> from one of the points and a <u>line across</u> from the other to make a <u>triangle</u>. The line drawn down the side of the triangle is the <u>change in y</u> and the line across the bottom is the <u>change in x</u>.

Change in y = 6.8 − 2.0 = 4.8 cm³   Change in x = 5.2 − 1.6 = 3.6 s

Rate = gradient = $\dfrac{\text{change in } y}{\text{change in } x} = \dfrac{4.8 \text{ cm}^3}{3.6 \text{ s}} = \underline{1.3 \text{ cm}^3 \text{ s}^{-1}}$

You can use this method to calculate other rates from a graph, not just the rate of a reaction. Just remember that a rate is how much something changes over time, so x needs to be the time.

The units of the gradient are (units of y)/(units of x). cm³ s⁻¹ can also be written as cm³/s.

2) To find the <u>gradient of a curve</u> at a <u>certain point</u>, draw a <u>tangent</u> to the curve at that point and then find the <u>gradient of the tangent</u>. See page 80 for details on how to do this.

3) The <u>intercept</u> of a graph is where the line of best fit crosses one of the <u>axes</u>. The <u>x-intercept</u> is where the line of best fit crosses the x-axis and the <u>y-intercept</u> is where it crosses the <u>y-axis</u>.

Graphs Show the Relationship Between Two Variables

1) You can get <u>three</u> types of <u>correlation</u> (relationship) between variables:

2) Just because there's correlation, it doesn't mean the change in one variable is <u>causing</u> the change in the other — there might be <u>other factors</u> involved (see page 10).

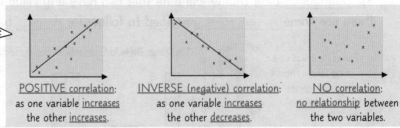

<u>POSITIVE</u> correlation: as one variable <u>increases</u> the other <u>increases</u>.

<u>INVERSE</u> (negative) correlation: as one variable <u>increases</u> the other <u>decreases</u>.

<u>NO</u> correlation: <u>no relationship</u> between the two variables.

I love eating apples — I call it core elation...

Science is all about finding relationships between things. And I don't mean that chemists gather together in corners to discuss whether or not Devini and Sebastian might be a couple... though they probably do that too.

Units and Equations

Graphs and maths skills are all very well, but the numbers don't mean much if you can't get the units right.

S.I. Units Are Used All Round the World

1) It wouldn't be all that useful if I defined volume in terms of bath tubs, you defined it in terms of egg-cups and my pal Sarwat defined it in terms of balloons — we'd never be able to compare our data.

2) To stop this happening, scientists have come up with a set of standard units, called S.I. units, that all scientists use to measure their data. Here are some S.I. units you'll see in chemistry:

Quantity	S.I. Base Unit
mass	kilogram, kg
length	metre, m
time	second, s
amount of a substance	mole, mol

Scaling Prefixes Can Be Used for Large and Small Quantities

1) Quantities come in a huge range of sizes. For example, the volume of a swimming pool might be around 2 000 000 000 cm³, while the volume of a cup is around 250 cm³.

2) To make the size of numbers more manageable, larger or smaller units are used. These are the S.I. base unit (e.g. metres) with a prefix in front:

prefix	tera (T)	giga (G)	mega (M)	kilo (k)	deci (d)	centi (c)	milli (m)	micro (µ)	nano (n)
multiple of unit	10^{12}	10^9	1 000 000 (10^6)	1000	0.1	0.01	0.001	0.000001 (10^{-6})	10^{-9}

3) These prefixes tell you how much bigger or smaller a unit is than the base unit. So one kilometre is one thousand metres.

> The conversion factor is the number of times the smaller unit goes into the larger unit.

4) To swap from one unit to another, all you need to know is what number you have to divide or multiply by to get from the original unit to the new unit — this is called the conversion factor.

- To go from a bigger unit (like m) to a smaller unit (like cm), you multiply by the conversion factor.
- To go from a smaller unit (like g) to a bigger unit (like kg), you divide by the conversion factor.

5) Here are some conversions that'll be useful for GCSE chemistry:

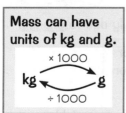
Mass can have units of kg and g.

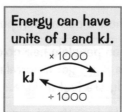
Energy can have units of J and kJ.

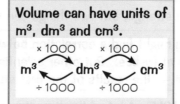
Volume can have units of m³, dm³ and cm³.

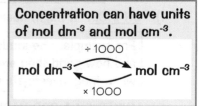
Concentration can have units of mol dm⁻³ and mol cm⁻³.

Always Check The Values Used in Equations Have the Right Units

1) Formulas and equations show relationships between variables.

2) To rearrange an equation, make sure that whatever you do to one side of the equation you also do to the other side.

> You can find the number of moles of something using the equation: moles = mass ÷ molar mass.
> You can rearrange this equation to find the mass by multiplying each side by molar mass to give: mass = moles × molar mass.

3) To use a formula, you need to know the values of all but one of the variables. Substitute the values you do know into the formula, and do the calculation to work out the final variable.

4) Always make sure the values you put into an equation or formula have the right units. For example, you might have done a titration experiment to work out the concentration of a solution. The volume of the solution will probably have been measured in cm³, but the equation to find concentration uses volume in dm³. So you'll have to convert your volume from cm³ to dm³ before you put it into the equation.

5) To make sure your units are correct, it can help to write down the units on each line of your calculation.

I wasn't sure I liked units, but now I'm converted...

It's easy to get in a muddle when converting between units, but there's a handy way to check you've done it right. If you're moving from a smaller unit to a larger unit (e.g. g to kg) the number should get smaller, and vice versa.

Drawing Conclusions

Congratulations — you're nearly at the end of a gruelling investigation, time to <u>draw conclusions</u>.

You Can Only Conclude What the Data Shows and NO MORE

1) Drawing conclusions might seem pretty straightforward — you just <u>look at your data</u> and <u>say what pattern or relationship you see</u> between the dependent and independent variables.

The table on the right shows the rate of a reaction in the presence of two <u>different</u> catalysts:

Catalyst	Rate of reaction (cm³ s⁻¹)
A	13.5
B	19.5
No catalyst	5.5

<u>CONCLUSION:</u>
Catalyst <u>B</u> makes <u>this reaction</u> go faster than catalyst A.

2) But you've got to be really careful that your conclusion <u>matches the data</u> you've got and <u>doesn't go any further</u>.

You <u>can't</u> conclude that catalyst B increases the rate of <u>any other reaction</u> more than catalyst A — the results might be completely different.

3) You also need to be able to <u>use your results</u> to <u>justify your conclusion</u> (i.e. back up your conclusion with some specific data).

The rate of this reaction was <u>6 cm³ s⁻¹ faster</u> using catalyst B compared with catalyst A.

4) When writing a conclusion you need to <u>refer back</u> to the original hypothesis and say whether the data <u>supports it</u> or not:

The hypothesis for this experiment might have been that catalyst B would make the reaction go <u>quicker</u> than catalyst A. If so, the data <u>supports</u> the hypothesis.

Correlation DOES NOT Mean Cause

If two things are correlated (i.e. there's a relationship between them) it <u>doesn't</u> necessarily mean a change in one variable is <u>causing</u> the change in the other — this is <u>REALLY IMPORTANT</u> — <u>DON'T FORGET IT</u>. There are <u>three possible reasons</u> for a correlation:

1) <u>CHANCE:</u> It might seem strange, but two things can show a correlation purely due to <u>chance</u>.

For example, one study might find a correlation between people's hair colour and how good they are at frisbee. But other scientists <u>don't</u> get a correlation when they investigate it — the results of the first study are just a <u>fluke</u>.

2) <u>LINKED BY A 3RD VARIABLE:</u> A lot of the time it may <u>look</u> as if a change in one variable is causing a change in the other, but it <u>isn't</u> — a <u>third variable links</u> the two things.

For example, there's a correlation between <u>water temperature</u> and <u>shark attacks</u>. This isn't because warmer water makes sharks crazy. Instead, they're linked by a third variable — the <u>number of people swimming</u> (more people swim when the water's hotter, and with more people in the water you get more shark attacks).

3) <u>CAUSE:</u> Sometimes a change in one variable does <u>cause</u> a change in the other. You can only conclude that a correlation is due to cause when you've <u>controlled all the variables</u> that could, just could, be affecting the result.

For example, there's a correlation between <u>smoking</u> and <u>lung cancer</u>. This is because chemicals in tobacco smoke cause lung cancer. This conclusion was only made once <u>other variables</u> (such as age and exposure to other things that cause cancer) had been <u>controlled</u> and shown <u>not</u> to affect people's risk of getting lung cancer.

I conclude that this page is a bit dull...

...although, just because I find it dull doesn't mean that I can conclude it's dull (you might think it's the most interesting thing since that kid got his head stuck in the railings near school). In the exams you could be given a conclusion and asked whether some data supports it — so make sure you understand how far conclusions can go.

Uncertainties and Evaluations

Hurrah! The end of another investigation. Well, now you have to work out all the things you did <u>wrong</u>.

Uncertainty is the Amount of Error Your Measurements Might Have

1) When you <u>repeat</u> a measurement, you often get a <u>slightly different</u> figure each time you do it due to <u>random error</u>. This means that <u>each result</u> has some <u>uncertainty</u> to it.

2) The measurements you make will also have some uncertainty in them due to <u>limits</u> in the <u>resolution</u> of the equipment you use (see page 6).

3) This all means that the <u>mean</u> of a set of results will also have some uncertainty to it. You can calculate the uncertainty of a <u>mean result</u> using the equation:

4) The <u>larger</u> the range, the <u>less precise</u> your results are and the <u>more uncertainty</u> there will be in your results. Uncertainties are shown using the '±' symbol.

The range is the largest value minus the smallest value (p.7).

$$\text{uncertainty} = \frac{\text{range}}{2}$$

 **EXAMPLE:** The table below shows the results of a titration experiment to determine the volume of 0.5 mol/dm³ sodium hydroxide solution needed to neutralise 25 cm³ of a solution of hydrochloric acid with unknown concentration. Calculate the uncertainty of the mean.

Repeat	1	2	3	mean
Volume of sodium hydroxide (cm³)	20.1	19.8	20.0	20.0

1) First work out the range:
Range = 20.1 − 19.8
= 0.300 cm³

2) Use the range to find the uncertainty:
Uncertainty = range ÷ 2 = 0.300 ÷ 2 = 0.150 cm³ So the uncertainty of the mean = 20.0 ± 0.2 cm³

5) Measuring a <u>greater amount</u> of something helps to <u>reduce uncertainty</u>. For example, in a rate of reaction experiment, measuring the amount of product formed over a <u>longer period</u> compared to a shorter period will <u>reduce</u> the <u>percentage uncertainty</u> in your results.

Evaluations — Describe How it Could be Improved

An evaluation is a <u>critical analysis</u> of the whole investigation.

1) You should comment on the <u>method</u> — was it <u>valid</u>? Did you control all the other variables to make it a <u>fair test</u>?

2) Comment on the <u>quality</u> of the <u>results</u> — was there <u>enough evidence</u> to reach a valid <u>conclusion</u>? Were the results <u>repeatable</u>, <u>reproducible</u>, <u>accurate</u> and <u>precise</u>?

3) Were there any <u>anomalous</u> results? If there were <u>none</u> then <u>say so</u>. If there were any, try to <u>explain</u> them — were they caused by <u>errors</u> in measurement? Were there any other <u>variables</u> that could have <u>affected</u> the results? You should comment on the level of <u>uncertainty</u> in your results too.

4) All this analysis will allow you to say how <u>confident</u> you are that your conclusion is <u>right</u>.

5) Then you can suggest any <u>changes</u> to the <u>method</u> that would <u>improve</u> the quality of the results, so that you could have <u>more confidence</u> in your conclusion. For example, you might suggest <u>changing</u> the way you controlled a variable, or <u>increasing</u> the number of <u>measurements</u> you took. Taking more measurements at <u>narrower intervals</u> could give you a <u>more accurate result</u>. For example:

<u>Enzymes</u> have an <u>optimum temperature</u> (a temperature at which they <u>work best</u>). Say you do an experiment to find an enzyme's optimum temperature and take measurements at 10 °C, 20 °C, 30 °C, 40 °C and 50 °C. The results of this experiment tell you the optimum is <u>40 °C</u>. You could then <u>repeat</u> the experiment, taking <u>more measurements around 40 °C</u> to a get a <u>more accurate</u> value for the optimum.

6) You could also make more <u>predictions</u> based on your conclusion, then <u>further experiments</u> could be carried out to test them.

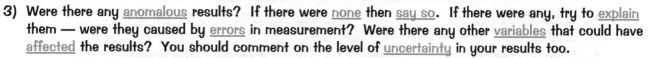

When suggesting improvements to the investigation, always make sure that you say why you think this would make the results better.

Evaluation — next time, I'll make sure I don't burn the lab down...

So there you have it — Working Scientifically. Make sure you know this stuff like the back of your hand. It's not just in the lab that you'll need to know how to work scientifically. You can be asked about it in the exams as well.

Chemical Equations

If you're going to get anywhere in chemistry you need to know about <u>chemical equations</u>...

Chemical Changes are Shown Using Chemical Equations

One way to show a chemical reaction is to write a <u>word equation</u>. It's not as <u>useful</u> as using chemical symbols because you can't tell straight away <u>what's happened</u> to each of the <u>atoms</u>, but it's <u>dead easy</u>.

Here's an example — <u>methane</u> burns in <u>oxygen</u> giving <u>carbon dioxide</u> and <u>water</u>:

The molecules on the <u>left-hand side</u> of the equation are called the <u>reactants</u> (because they react with each other).

methane + oxygen → carbon dioxide + water

The molecules on the <u>right-hand side</u> are called the <u>products</u> (because they've been produced from the reactants).

Symbol Equations Show the Atoms on Both Sides

Chemical <u>changes</u> can be shown in a kind of <u>shorthand</u> using symbol equations. Symbol equations just show the <u>symbols</u> or <u>formulas</u> of the <u>reactants</u> and <u>products</u>...

$$\text{magnesium} + \text{oxygen} \rightarrow \text{magnesium oxide}$$
$$2Mg + O_2 \rightarrow 2MgO$$

Symbol Equations Need to be Balanced

1) There must always be the <u>same</u> number of atoms of each element on <u>both sides</u> of the equation — atoms can't just <u>disappear</u>.

2) You <u>balance</u> the equation by putting numbers <u>in front</u> of the formulas where needed. Take this equation for reacting sulfuric acid with sodium hydroxide:

$$H_2SO_4 + NaOH \rightarrow Na_2SO_4 + H_2O$$

3) The <u>formulas</u> are all correct but the numbers of some atoms <u>don't match up</u> on both sides.

4) You <u>can't change formulas</u> like H_2SO_4 to H_2SO_5. You can only put numbers <u>in front of them</u>.

5) The more you <u>practise</u>, the <u>quicker</u> you get, but all you do is this:

- Find an element that <u>doesn't balance</u> and <u>pencil in a number</u> to try and sort it out.
- <u>See where it gets you</u>. It may create <u>another imbalance</u>, but if so, pencil in <u>another number</u> and see where that gets you.
- Carry on chasing <u>unbalanced</u> elements and it'll <u>sort itself out</u> pretty quickly.

EXAMPLE: In the equation above you'll notice you're short of <u>H atoms</u> on the RHS (Right-Hand Side).

1) The only thing you can do about that is make it <u>2H₂O</u> instead of just H_2O:
$$H_2SO_4 + NaOH \rightarrow Na_2SO_4 + 2H_2O$$

2) But that now gives <u>too many</u> H atoms and O atoms on the RHS, so to balance that up you could try putting a <u>2</u> in front of the <u>NaOH</u> on the LHS (Left-Hand Side):
$$H_2SO_4 + 2NaOH \rightarrow Na_2SO_4 + 2H_2O$$

Putting a 2 in front of the NaOH has sorted out the Na atoms too.

3) And suddenly there it is — <u>everything balances</u>.

Revision is all about getting the balance right...

Balancing equations is all about practice. Once you have a few goes you'll see it's much less scary than it seemed before you took on, challenged and defeated this page. Go grab some chemistry glory.

Q1   Balance the equation: $Fe + Cl_2 \rightarrow FeCl_3$ [1 mark]

Q2   Hydrogen and oxygen molecules are formed in a reaction where water splits apart.
      For this reaction: a) State the word equation.   b) Give a balanced symbol equation.   [3 marks]

Chemical Equations Involving Ions

If you thought that was all there was to know about <u>chemical equations</u>, prepare to be sorely disappointed...

State Symbols Tell You the State of a Substance in an Equation

You saw on the last page how a chemical reaction can be shown using a <u>word equation</u> or a <u>symbol equation</u>. Symbol equations can also include <u>state symbols</u> next to each substance — they tell you what <u>physical state</u> (see page 34) the reactants and products are in:

> (s) — solid   (l) — liquid   (g) — gas   (aq) — aqueous

'Aqueous' means 'dissolved in water'.

> **Example:** Aqueous hydrochloric acid reacts with solid calcium carbonate to form aqueous calcium chloride, liquid water and carbon dioxide gas: $2HCl_{(aq)} + CaCO_{3(s)} \rightarrow CaCl_{2(aq)} + H_2O_{(l)} + CO_{2(g)}$

You Need to Learn the Formulas of Some Simple Compounds and Ions

1) It's a good idea to <u>learn</u> the chemical formulas of these common molecules. They crop up all the time.

> - Water — H_2O
> - Ammonia — NH_3
> - Carbon dioxide — CO_2
> - Hydrogen — H_2
> - Chlorine — Cl_2
> - Oxygen — O_2

2) You also need to be able to recall the formulas of <u>certain ions</u>.

3) For <u>single atoms</u>, you can use the periodic table to work out what <u>charges</u> their ions will form (see page 20).

Ions form when atoms, or groups of atoms, gain or lose electrons to form charged particles (see page 20).

4) For ions made up of groups of atoms, it's not so simple. You just have to <u>learn</u> these ones.

> - Ammonium — NH_4^+
> - Hydroxide — OH^-
> - Nitrate — NO_3^-
> - Carbonate — CO_3^{2-}
> - Sulfate — SO_4^{2-}

Ionic Equations Show Just the Useful Bits of Reactions

1) You can also write an <u>ionic equation</u> for any reaction involving ions that happens in solution.

2) In an ionic equation, only the <u>reacting particles</u> (and the products they form) are included.

3) To write an ionic equation, all you need to do is look at the balanced symbol equation and take out any <u>aqueous ions</u> that are present on <u>both sides</u> of the equation.

You should make sure your symbol equation is balanced before you start trying to write the ionic equation (see the last page for more on how to balance symbol equations).

EXAMPLE: Write the ionic equation for the following reaction:
$$CaCl_{2(aq)} + 2NaOH_{(aq)} \rightarrow Ca(OH)_{2(s)} + 2NaCl_{(aq)}$$

1) Anything that's <u>ionic</u> (i.e. made of ions — see page 20) and <u>aqueous</u> will break up into its ions in solution. So, write out the equation showing all the <u>aqueous ions</u> separately.
$$Ca^{2+}_{(aq)} + 2Cl^-_{(aq)} + 2Na^+_{(aq)} + 2OH^-_{(aq)} \rightarrow Ca(OH)_{2(s)} + 2Na^+_{(aq)} + 2Cl^-_{(aq)}$$

2) To get to the ionic equation, <u>cross out</u> anything that's the <u>same on both sides</u> of the equation — here, that's the Na^+ and Cl^- ions.
$$Ca^{2+}_{(aq)} + 2Cl^-_{(aq)} + 2Na^+_{(aq)} + 2OH^-_{(aq)} \rightarrow Ca(OH)_{2(s)} + 2Na^+_{(aq)} + 2Cl^-_{(aq)}$$

$$Ca^{2+}_{(aq)} + 2OH^-_{(aq)} \rightarrow Ca(OH)_{2(s)}$$

The overall charge should be the same on both sides. Here, charge on RHS = 0 and charge on LHS $= (2+) + (2 \times 1-) = 0$.

I'm in a Texan percussion band — we're called the state cymbals...

Ionic equations are trouble if you ask me. All those pesky ions messing things up. Better get some practice in...

Q1   Write the ionic equation for the following reaction: $HNO_{3(aq)} + NaOH_{(aq)} \rightarrow NaNO_{3(aq)} + H_2O_{(l)}$ [1 mark]

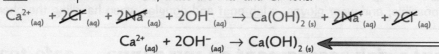

Hazards and Risk

Chemistry's a risky business. It's not like maths, where the most dangerous thing you might come across is an awkward long division. When you're doing chemistry, you could be dealing with properly dangerous chemicals...

You Need to Learn the Common Hazard Symbols

1) A hazard is anything that has the potential to cause harm or damage. The risk associated with that hazard is the probability of someone (or something) being harmed if they are exposed to the hazard.

2) Lots of the chemicals you'll meet in chemistry can be bad for you or dangerous in some way. That's why the chemical containers will normally have symbols on them to tell you what the dangers are.

3) Understanding these symbols means you'll be able to use suitable safe-working procedures in the lab.

Oxidising
Provides oxygen which allows other materials to burn more fiercely.
Example: Liquid oxygen.

Harmful
Can cause irritation, reddening or blistering of the skin.
Example: Bleach.

Environmental Hazard
Harmful to organisms and to the environment.
Example: Mercury.

Highly Flammable
Catches fire easily.
Example: Petrol.

Toxic
Can cause death by, e.g. swallowing, breathing in, absorption through skin.
Example: Hydrogen cyanide.

Corrosive
Destroys materials, including living tissues (e.g. eyes and skin).
Example: Concentrated sulfuric acid.

Experiments Involve Risks and Hazards

1) Many chemistry experiments have risks associated with them. These can include risks associated with the equipment you're using (e.g. the risk of burning from an electric heater) as well as risks associated with chemicals (see above).

2) When you plan an experiment, you need to identify all the hazards and what the risk is from each hazard. This includes working out how likely it is that something could go wrong, and how serious it would be if it did. You then need to think of ways to reduce these risks. This procedure is called a risk assessment.

> Err... Doug, it's meant to be a risk assessment

Example: A student is going to react a solution of sodium hydroxide with hydrochloric acid to form a metal salt and water. Identify any hazards in this experiment, and suggest how they could reduce the risk.

Sodium hydroxide and hydrochloric acid are harmful at low concentrations and corrosive at high concentrations. Harmful substances can cause blistering or reddening of the skin, but corrosive substances are much more dangerous if they come into contact with your skin or eyes.
To reduce the risks posed by these hazards, the student should try to use low concentrations of the substances if possible, and wear gloves, a lab coat and goggles when handling the chemicals.

I always carry out a risk assessment on my cuppa — safe-tea first...

Not only do you need to know this stuff for your exam, you need to know it if you're going to safely carry out any experiments in the lab. With all those dangerous chemicals, this page just might save you from a nasty accident.

Q1 A student is carrying out an experiment using two chemicals. Chemical A is corrosive while chemical B is highly flammable. Suggest appropriate safety precautions the student could take to minimise the risk associated with the chemicals. [2 marks]

The History of the Atom

Atoms are pretty tiny. But what exactly are they like? Scientists have been trying to work it out for years...

The Theory of Atomic Structure Has Changed

Atoms are the tiny particles of matter (stuff that has a mass) which make up everything in the universe...

1) At the start of the 19th century, John Dalton described atoms as solid spheres, and said that different spheres made up the different elements.

2) In 1897, J J Thomson concluded from his experiments that atoms weren't solid spheres. His measurements of charge and mass showed that an atom must contain even smaller, negatively charged particles — electrons. The 'solid sphere' idea of atomic structure had to be changed. The new theory was known as the 'plum pudding model'.

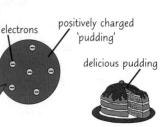

electrons — positively charged 'pudding'

delicious pudding

Rutherford Showed that the Plum Pudding Model Was Wrong

1) In 1909, Ernest Rutherford and his students, Hans Geiger and Ernest Marsden, conducted the famous gold foil experiment. They fired positively charged alpha particles at an extremely thin sheet of gold.

2) From the plum pudding model, they were expecting the particles to pass straight through the sheet or be slightly deflected at most. This was because the positive charge of each atom was thought to be very spread out through the 'pudding' of the atom. But, whilst most of the particles did go straight through the gold sheet, some were deflected more than expected, and a small number were deflected backwards. So the plum pudding model couldn't be right.

3) Rutherford came up with the theory of the nuclear atom to explain this new evidence. In this, there's a tiny, positively charged nucleus at the centre, surrounded by a 'cloud' of negative electrons — most of the atom's empty space.

A few particles are deflected backwards by the nucleus.

Most of the particles pass through empty space.

The Refined Bohr Model Explains a Lot

1) Scientists realised that electrons in a 'cloud' around the nucleus of an atom, as Rutherford described, would be attracted to the nucleus, causing the atom to collapse. Niels Bohr proposed a new model of the atom where all the electrons were contained in shells.

nucleus — shells

electrons

2) Bohr suggested that electrons can only exist in fixed orbits, or shells, and not anywhere in between. Each shell has a fixed energy.

3) Bohr's theory of atomic structure was supported by many experiments and it helped to explain lots of other scientists' observations at the time. It was pretty close to our currently accepted version of the atom (see next page).

Scientific Theories Have to be Backed Up by Evidence

1) So, our current model of the atom is completely different to what people thought the atom looked like in the past. These different ideas were accepted because they fitted the evidence available at the time.

2) As scientists did more experiments, new evidence was found and our theory of the structure of the atom was modified to fit it. This is nearly always the way scientific knowledge develops — new evidence prompts people to come up with new, improved ideas. These ideas can be used to make predictions which, if proved correct, are a pretty good indication that the ideas are right.

3) Scientists also put their ideas and research up for peer review. This means everyone gets a chance to see the new ideas, check for errors and then other scientists can use it to help develop their own work.

I love a good model — Kate Moss is my personal favourite...

This is a great example of how science works. Scientists working together to find evidence. Lovely.

Q1   Describe the gold foil experiment and how it disproved the plum pudding model of the atom.   [4 marks]

Q2   Draw and label a diagram to show the Bohr model of the atom.   [2 marks]

The Atom

All substances are made of atoms. They're really tiny — too small to see, even with a microscope.

Atoms Contain Protons, Neutrons and Electrons

The atom is made up of three subatomic particles — protons, neutrons and electrons.

- Protons are heavy and positively charged.
- Neutrons are heavy and neutral.
- Electrons have hardly any mass and are negatively charged.

Particle	Relative mass	Relative charge
Proton	1	+1
Neutron	1	0
Electron	0.0005	−1

Relative mass (measured in atomic mass units) measures mass on a scale where the mass of a proton or neutron is 1.

Protons and neutrons are still teeny tiny — they're just heavy compared to electrons.

The Nucleus

1) It's in the middle of the atom.
2) It contains protons and neutrons.
3) It has a positive charge because of the protons.
4) Almost the whole mass of the atom is concentrated in the nucleus.
5) Compared to the overall size of the atom, the nucleus is tiny.

The Electrons

1) Electrons move around the nucleus in electron shells.
2) They're negatively charged.
3) They're tiny, but their shells cover a lot of space.
4) The size of their shells determines the size of the atom. Atoms have a radius (known as the atomic radius) of about 10^{-10} m.
5) Electrons have a tiny mass (so small that it's sometimes given as zero).

Houston, we're in orbit.

In an Atom the Number of Protons Equals the Number of Electrons

1) Atoms are neutral — they have no charge overall (unlike ions).
2) This is because they have the same number of protons as electrons.
3) The charge on the electrons is the same size as the charge on the protons, but opposite — so the charges cancel out.
4) In an ion, the number of protons doesn't equal the number of electrons. This means it has an overall charge. For example, an ion with a 2− charge, has two more electrons than protons.

An ion is an atom or group of atoms that has lost or gained electrons.

Atomic Number and Mass Number Describe an Atom

1) The nuclear symbol of an atom tells you its atomic (proton) number and mass number.
2) The atomic number tells you how many protons an atom has. Every atom of an element has the same number of protons.
3) For a neutral atom, the number of protons equals the number of electrons, so the number of electrons equals the atomic number.
4) The mass number tells you the total number of protons and neutrons in the atom.
5) To work out the number of neutrons in an atom, just subtract the atomic number from the mass number.

Nuclear symbol for sodium.

Mass number → 23
Atomic number → 11
Na
Element symbol

Don't trust atoms — they make up everything...

You need to learn what's in that table with the relative masses and relative charges of the different parts of the atom.

Q1   A certain neutral atom of potassium has an atomic number of 19 and a mass number of 39.
       Give the number of electrons, protons and neutrons in the atom.

[3 marks]

Isotopes and Relative Atomic Mass

Atoms were reasonably straightforward weren't they? Think again. Here come <u>isotopes</u> to confuse everything.

Isotopes are the Same Except for Extra Neutrons

1) <u>Isotopes</u> are different forms of the same element, which have the <u>same number</u> of <u>protons</u> but a <u>different number</u> of <u>neutrons</u>.

2) So isotopes have the <u>same atomic number</u> but <u>different mass numbers</u>.

3) A very popular example of a pair of isotopes is <u>carbon-12</u> and <u>carbon-13</u>.

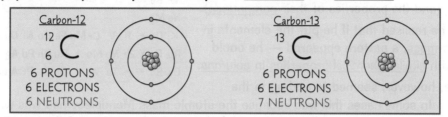

Carbon-12
$^{12}_{6}C$
6 PROTONS
6 ELECTRONS
6 NEUTRONS

Carbon-13
$^{13}_{6}C$
6 PROTONS
6 ELECTRONS
7 NEUTRONS

Remember — the number of neutrons is just the mass number minus the atomic number.

Relative Atomic Mass Takes Isotopes Into Account

1) In the periodic table, the elements all have <u>two</u> numbers next to them. The <u>bigger one</u> is the <u>relative atomic mass</u> (A_r) of the element.

> The <u>relative atomic mass</u> of an element is the <u>average mass</u> of <u>one atom</u> of the element, compared to $\frac{1}{12}$ of the <u>mass</u> of <u>one atom</u> of <u>carbon-12</u>.

relative atomic mass

$^{4}_{2}He$ $^{12}_{6}C$

2) If an element only has <u>one isotope</u>, its A_r will be the same as its <u>mass number</u> (see last page).

3) If an element has <u>more than one</u> isotope, its A_r is the <u>average</u> of the <u>mass numbers</u> of <u>all the different isotopes</u>, taking into account <u>how much</u> there is of each one. So, it might not be a whole number.

> For example, chlorine has two stable isotopes, <u>chlorine-35</u> and <u>chlorine-37</u>. There's <u>quite a lot</u> of chlorine-35 around and <u>not so much</u> chlorine-37 — so chlorine's A_r works out as <u>35.5</u>.

A_r Can Be Worked Out from Isotopic Abundances

1) Different isotopes of an element occur in different quantities, or <u>isotopic abundances</u>.

2) You need to know how to <u>calculate</u> the <u>relative atomic mass</u> of an element from its <u>isotopic abundances</u>.

3) To work out the relative atomic mass of an element, you need to find the <u>average mass</u> of <u>all its atoms</u>. Here's how...

> • <u>Multiply</u> each <u>relative isotopic mass</u> by its <u>isotopic abundance</u>, and <u>add up</u> the results.
> • <u>Divide</u> by the <u>sum</u> of the <u>abundances</u>. (If the abundances are given as percentages, this will be 100.)

EXAMPLE:

Boron has two isotopes, boron-10 and boron-11.
Given that the relative abundances of boron-10 and boron-11 are 4 and 16 respectively, work out the relative atomic mass of boron.

1) Multiply each <u>relative isotopic mass</u> by its <u>relative abundance</u>, then add up the results.

$(10 \times 4) + (11 \times 16) = 216$

2) Divide this by the <u>sum</u> of the <u>isotopic abundances</u>.

$216 \div (16 + 4) = 10.8$

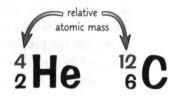

It's elemental my dear Watson...

Atoms, elements and isotopes — make sure you know what they are and the differences between them.

Q1   Bromine has an atomic number of 35 and has two stable isotopes — bromine-79 and bromine-81.
      Given that 51% of bromine atoms are bromine-79, and 49% are bromine-81,
      work out the relative atomic mass of bromine. Give your answer to the nearest whole number.   [2 marks]

The Periodic Table

We haven't always known as much about chemistry as we do now. No sirree. Take the periodic table.
Early chemists looked to try and find patterns in the elements' properties to understand a bit more about them.

Dmitri Mendeleev Made the First Proper Periodic Table

1) In 1869, Dmitri Mendeleev arranged the 50 or so
   elements known at the time into a Table of Elements.

2) He began by sorting the elements into groups, based on
   their properties (and the properties of their compounds).

3) As he did this, he realised that if he put the elements in
   order of atomic mass, a pattern appeared — he could
   put elements with similar chemical properties in columns.

Mendeleev's Table of the Elements

```
H
Li  Be                                    B  C  N  O  F
Na  Mg                                    Al Si P  S  Cl
K  Ca *  Ti V  Cr Mn Fe Co Ni Cu Zn *  *  As Se Br
Rb Sr Y  Zr Nb Mo *  Ru Rh Pd Ag Cd In Sn Sb Te I
Cs Ba *  *  Ta W  *  Os Ir Pt Au Hg Tl Pb Bi
```

4) A few elements, however, seemed to end up in the
   wrong columns. In some cases this was because the atomic mass Mendeleev had was wrong (due to the
   presence of isotopes) — but some elements just didn't quite fit the pattern. Wherever this happened,
   he switched the order of the elements to keep those with the same properties in the same columns.

5) To keep elements with similar properties together, Mendeleev also had to leave some gaps (shown by
   the *s in the table above). He used the properties of the other elements in the columns with the gaps
   to predict the properties of undiscovered elements. When they were found and they fitted the pattern,
   it helped to confirm his ideas. For example, Mendeleev predicted the chemical and physical properties
   of an element he called ekasilicon, which we know today as germanium.

This is How the Periodic Table Looks Today

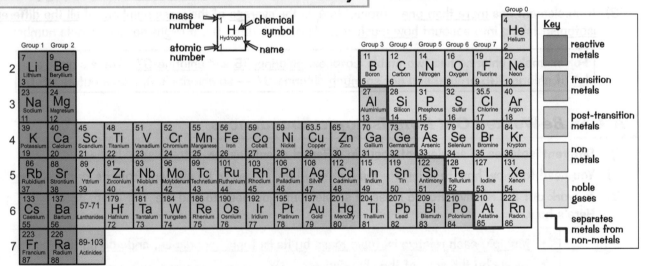

1) Once protons and electrons were discovered, the atomic number (see p.16) of each element could be
   found, based on the number of protons in its nucleus. The modern periodic table shows the elements in
   order of ascending atomic number — and they fit the same patterns that Mendeleev worked out.

2) The periodic table is laid out so elements with similar chemical properties form columns called groups.

3) The group to which the element belongs corresponds to the number of electrons it has in its outer shell.
   E.g. Group 1 elements have 1 outer shell electron, Group 7 elements have 7, etc. Group 0 elements
   are the exception — they have full outer shells of 8 electrons (or 2 in the case of helium).

4) The rows are called periods. Each new period represents another full shell of electrons (see next page).

5) The period to which the element belongs corresponds to the number of shells of electrons it has.

These jokes are tested for funniness — periodically...

You can use your old mate the periodic table to make predictions about how reactions will occur. How neat is that?

Q1   Based on its position in the periodic table, would you expect the chemical properties
      of potassium to be more similar to those of sodium or calcium? Explain your answer.   [2 marks]

Electronic Configurations

Like snails, <u>electrons</u> live in <u>shells</u>. Unlike snails, electrons won't nibble on your petunias...

Electron Shell Rules:

1) Electrons always occupy <u>shells</u> (sometimes called <u>energy levels</u>).
2) The <u>lowest</u> energy levels are <u>always filled first</u>.
3) Only <u>a certain number</u> of electrons are allowed in each shell:

1st shell	2nd shell	3rd shell
<u>2</u> electrons	<u>8</u> electrons	<u>8</u> electrons

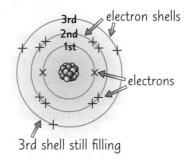

electron shells

electrons

3rd shell still filling

Working Out Electronic Configurations

The <u>electronic configurations</u> of the first <u>20</u> elements are shown in the diagram below.
They're not hard to work out. For a quick example, take nitrogen:

1) The periodic table tells you that the atomic number of nitrogen is <u>seven</u>.
   That means nitrogen has seven protons, so it must have <u>seven electrons</u>.

2) Follow the '<u>Electron Shell Rules</u>' above. The <u>first</u> shell can only take 2 electrons and the <u>second</u> shell can take a <u>maximum</u> of 8 electrons. So the electronic configuration of nitrogen must be <u>2.5</u>.

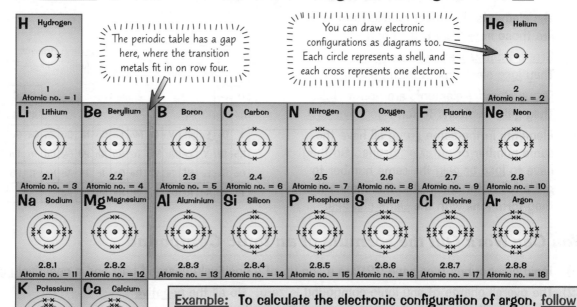

The periodic table has a gap here, where the transition metals fit in on row four.

You can draw electronic configurations as diagrams too. Each circle represents a shell, and each cross represents one electron.

Example: To calculate the electronic configuration of argon, <u>follow the rules</u>. It's got 18 protons, so it <u>must</u> have 18 electrons. The first shell must have <u>2</u> electrons, the second shell must have <u>8</u>, and so the third shell must have <u>8</u> as well. It's as easy as <u>2.8.8</u>.

You can also work out the electronic configuration of an element from its <u>period</u> and <u>group</u>.

• The <u>number of shells</u> which contain electrons is the same as the <u>period</u> of the element.
• The <u>group number</u> tells you <u>how many electrons</u> occupy the <u>outer shell</u> of the element.

<u>Example:</u> Sodium is in <u>period 3</u>, so it has <u>3</u> shells occupied. The first two shells must be full (2.8). It's in <u>Group 1</u>, so it has <u>1</u> electron in its outer shell. So its electronic configuration is <u>2.8.1</u>.

The electronic configuration of the fifth element — it's a bit boron...

Electronic configurations may seem a bit complicated at first but once you learn the rules, it's a piece of cake.

Q1　Give the electronic configuration of aluminium (atomic number = 13). 　　　　　　　[1 mark]

Q2　In which group and period of the periodic table would you expect
　　　to find the element with the electronic configuration 2.8.8.2? 　　　　　　　[2 marks]

Ions

Some atoms are keen on getting rid of some of their <u>electrons</u>. Others want more. That's life. And <u>ions</u>...

Simple Ions Form When Atoms Lose or Gain Electrons

1) <u>Ions</u> are <u>charged</u> particles — they can be <u>single atoms</u> (e.g. Na^+) or <u>groups of atoms</u> (e.g. NO_3^-).

2) When <u>atoms</u> lose or gain electrons to form ions, all they're trying to do is get a <u>full outer shell</u> (also called a "<u>stable electronic structure</u>"). Atoms like full outer shells — it's atom heaven.

3) <u>Negative ions</u> (anions) form when atoms <u>gain electrons</u> — they have more electrons than protons. <u>Positive ions</u> (cations) form when atoms <u>lose electrons</u> — they have more protons than electrons.

4) The <u>number</u> of electrons lost or gained is the same as the <u>charge</u> on the ion. E.g. If 2 electrons are <u>lost</u> the charge is 2+. If 3 electrons are <u>gained</u> the charge is 3–.

> You calculate the number of protons and neutrons in an ion in the same way as for an atom (see page 16).

- F^- has a <u>single negative charge</u>, so it must have one more electron than protons. F has an atomic number of 9, so has 9 protons. So F^- must have 9 + 1 = <u>10 electrons</u>.
- Fe^{2+} has a <u>2+ charge</u>, so it must have two more protons than electrons. Fe has an atomic number of 26, so has 26 protons. So Fe^{2+} must have 26 – 2 = <u>24 electrons</u>.

Groups 1 & 2 and 6 & 7 are the Most Likely to Form Ions

1) The elements that most readily form ions are those in <u>Groups 1</u>, <u>2</u>, <u>6</u> and <u>7</u>.

2) <u>Group 1 and 2 elements</u> are <u>metals</u>. They <u>lose</u> electrons to form <u>positive ions</u>.

3) <u>Group 6 and 7 elements</u> are <u>non-metals</u>. They <u>gain</u> electrons to form <u>negative ions</u>.

4) Elements in the same <u>group</u> all have the same number of <u>outer electrons</u>. So they have to <u>lose or gain</u> the same number to get a full outer shell. And this means that they form ions with the <u>same charges</u>.

Group 1 elements form 1+ ions.
Group 2 elements form 2+ ions.
Group 6 elements form 2– ions.
Group 7 elements form 1– ions.

H																	He
Li	Be											B	C	N	O	F	Ne
Na	Mg											Al	Si	P	S	Cl	Ar
K	Ca	Sc	Ti	V	Cr	Mn	Fe	Co	Ni	Cu	Zn	Ga	Ge	As	Se	Br	Kr
Rb	Sr	Y	Zr	Nb	Mo	Tc	Ru	Rh	Pd	Ag	Cd	In	Sn	Sb	Te	I	Xe
Cs	Ba	La	Hf	Ta	W	Re	Os	Ir	Pt	Au	Hg	Tl	Pb	Bi	Po	At	Rn
Fr	Ra	Ac	Rf	Db	Sg	Bh	Hs	Mt	Ds	Rg							

You Can Work Out the Formula of an Ionic Compound

1) Ionic compounds (see page 22) are made up of a <u>positively charged</u> part and a <u>negatively charged</u> part.

2) The <u>overall charge</u> of <u>any ionic compound</u> is <u>zero</u>. So all the <u>negative charges</u> in the compound must <u>balance</u> all the <u>positive charges</u>.

3) You can use the charges on the <u>individual ions</u> present to work out the formula for the ionic compound.

4) You need to be able to write formulas using <u>chemical symbols</u>.

> Ions with names ending in -ate (e.g. nitrate) are negative ions containing oxygen and at least one other element. Ions with names ending in -ide (e.g. chloride) are negative ions containing only one element (apart from hydroxide ions which are OH^-).

EXAMPLE: What is the chemical formula of calcium nitrate?

1) Write out the <u>formulas</u> of the calcium and nitrate ions. Ca^{2+}, NO_3^-

2) The <u>overall charge</u> on the formula must be <u>zero</u>, so work out the ratio of Ca : NO_3 that gives an overall neutral charge.

To balance the 2+ charge on Ca^{2+}, you need two NO_3^- ions: (+2) + (2 × –1) = 0. The formula is $Ca(NO_3)_2$

> The brackets show you need two of the whole nitrate ion.

Magnesium sulfide isn't sarcastic, it's just an ironic compound...

Don't forget about ions made up of groups of atoms, like the ones on page 13. You can't use the periodic table to work out the charges on these, like you can with the elements in Groups 1, 2, 6 and 7. You just need to learn them.

Q1   What is the formula of the ionic compound, lithium oxide?   [1 mark]

Ionic Bonding

Time to find out how particles bond together to form compounds (bet you can't wait). There are <u>three</u> types of bonding you need to know about — <u>ionic</u>, <u>covalent</u> and <u>metallic</u>. First up, it's <u>ionic bonds</u>.

Ionic Bonding — Transfer of Electrons

When a <u>metal</u> and a <u>non-metal</u> react together, the <u>metal atom loses</u> electrons to form a <u>positive ion</u> (cation) and the <u>non-metal gains these electrons</u> to form a <u>negative ion</u> (anion). These oppositely charged ions are <u>strongly attracted</u> to one another by <u>electrostatic forces</u>. This attraction is called an <u>ionic bond</u>.

Use Dot and Cross Diagrams to Show How Ionic Compounds are Formed

<u>Dot and cross diagrams</u> show the <u>arrangement</u> of electrons in an atom or ion. Each electron is represented by a <u>dot</u> or a <u>cross</u>. So these diagrams can show which <u>atom</u> the electrons in an <u>ion</u> originally came from.

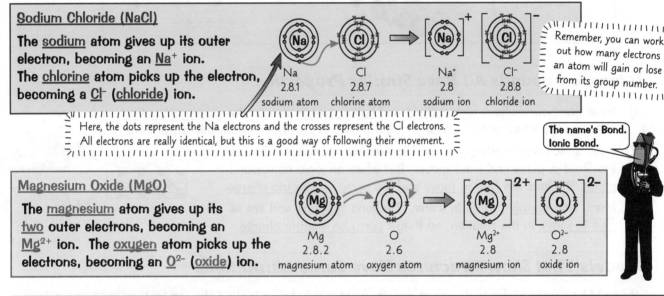

<u>Sodium Chloride (NaCl)</u>

The <u>sodium</u> atom gives up its outer electron, becoming an <u>Na+</u> ion.
The <u>chlorine</u> atom picks up the electron, becoming a <u>Cl−</u> (<u>chloride</u>) ion.

Na 2.8.1 sodium atom
Cl 2.8.7 chlorine atom
Na+ 2.8 sodium ion
Cl− 2.8.8 chloride ion

Remember, you can work out how many electrons an atom will gain or lose from its group number.

Here, the dots represent the Na electrons and the crosses represent the Cl electrons. All electrons are really identical, but this is a good way of following their movement.

The name's Bond.
Ionic Bond.

<u>Magnesium Oxide (MgO)</u>

The <u>magnesium</u> atom gives up its <u>two</u> outer electrons, becoming an <u>Mg2+</u> ion. The <u>oxygen</u> atom picks up the electrons, becoming an <u>O2−</u> (<u>oxide</u>) ion.

Mg 2.8.2 magnesium atom
O 2.6 oxygen atom
Mg2+ 2.8 magnesium ion
O2− 2.8 oxide ion

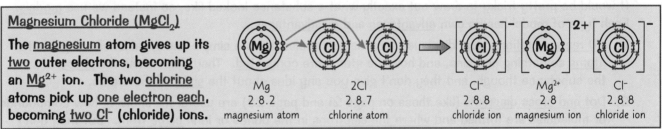

<u>Magnesium Chloride (MgCl₂)</u>

The <u>magnesium</u> atom gives up its <u>two</u> outer electrons, becoming an <u>Mg2+</u> ion. The two <u>chlorine</u> atoms pick up <u>one electron each</u>, becoming <u>two Cl−</u> (<u>chloride</u>) ions.

Mg 2.8.2 magnesium atom
2Cl 2.8.7 chlorine atom
Cl− 2.8.8 chloride ion
Mg2+ 2.8 magnesium ion
Cl− 2.8.8 chloride ion

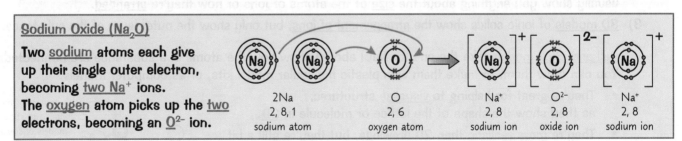

<u>Sodium Oxide (Na₂O)</u>

Two <u>sodium</u> atoms each give up their single outer electron, becoming <u>two Na+</u> ions.
The <u>oxygen</u> atom picks up the <u>two</u> electrons, becoming an <u>O2−</u> ion.

2Na 2, 8, 1 sodium atom
O 2, 6 oxygen atom
Na+ 2, 8 sodium ion
O2− 2, 8 oxide ion
Na+ 2, 8 sodium ion

Any old ion, any old ion — any, any, any old ion...

You need to be able to describe how ionic compounds are formed using both words and dot and cross diagrams. It gets easier with practice, so here are some questions to get you started.

Q1   Describe, in terms of electron transfer, how sodium (Na) and chlorine (Cl)
      react to form sodium chloride (NaCl).   [3 marks]

Q2   Draw a dot and cross diagram to show how potassium (electronic configuration 2.8.8.1)
      and chlorine (electronic configuration 2.8.7) form potassium chloride (KCl).   [3 marks]

Ionic Compounds

I know it's covered in <u>sodium chloride</u>, but this page is all true — no need to take it with a pinch of salt...

Ionic Compounds Have a Regular Lattice Structure

<u>Ionic compounds</u> always have <u>giant ionic lattice</u> structures. The ions form a closely packed <u>regular lattice</u>. There are very strong <u>electrostatic forces of attraction</u> between <u>oppositely charged</u> ions, in <u>all directions</u>.

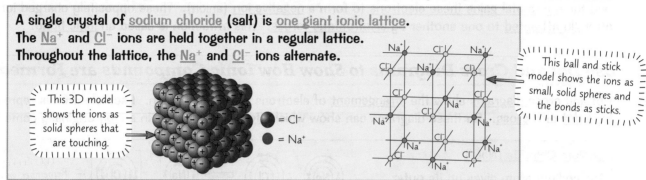

A single crystal of <u>sodium chloride</u> (salt) is <u>one giant ionic lattice</u>. The Na^+ and Cl^- ions are held together in a regular lattice. Throughout the lattice, the Na^+ and Cl^- ions alternate.

This 3D model shows the ions as solid spheres that are touching.

● = Cl^-
● = Na^+

This ball and stick model shows the ions as small, solid spheres and the bonds as sticks.

Ionic Compounds All Have Similar Properties

1) Ionic compounds have <u>high melting</u> and <u>boiling points</u> due to the <u>strong attraction</u> between the ions. It takes a large amount of <u>energy</u> to overcome this attraction.

2) Solid ionic compounds <u>don't</u> conduct electricity because the ions are fixed in place and can't move. But when an ionic compound <u>melts</u>, the ions are <u>free to move</u> and will <u>carry an electric charge</u>.

3) Many also <u>dissolve easily</u> in water. The ions <u>separate</u> and are all <u>free to move</u> in the solution, so they'll <u>carry an electric charge</u>.

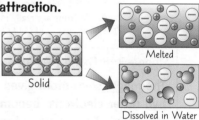

Solid
Melted
Dissolved in Water

Models That Show Structures Have Some Limitations

It would be pretty tricky to draw out exactly what a substance looked like, so instead we use <u>models</u>. Each type of model has its own <u>advantages</u> and <u>disadvantages</u>...

1) <u>2D representations</u> (e.g. displayed formulas) of molecules are simple and great at showing what <u>atoms</u> something contains, and how the atoms are <u>connected</u>. They don't show the <u>shape</u> of the substance though, and they don't give you any idea about the <u>sizes</u> of the atoms.

2) <u>Dot and cross diagrams</u> (like those on page 21 and page 23) are useful for showing how compounds or molecules are formed and <u>where the electrons</u> in the bonds or ions <u>came from</u>. But they <u>don't</u> usually show you anything about the <u>size</u> of the atoms or ions or how they're <u>arranged</u>.

3) <u>3D models</u> of ionic solids show the <u>arrangement of ions</u>, but only show the outer layer of the substance.

<u>Ball and stick models</u> (like the one for NaCl above) show how the atoms in a substance are connected. You can draw them, or make them with plastic molecular model kits, or as computer models.

- They're great for helping to <u>visualise</u> structures, as they show the shape of the lattice or molecule in <u>3D</u>.
- They're <u>more realistic</u> than 2D drawings, but they're still a bit <u>misleading</u>. They make it look like there are <u>big gaps</u> between the atoms — in reality this is where the <u>electron clouds</u> interact.
- They also don't show the <u>correct scales</u> of the atoms or ions. The atoms and ions are really different sizes, but this isn't shown well by ball and stick models.

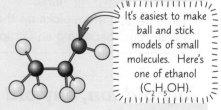

It's easiest to make ball and stick models of small molecules. Here's one of ethanol (C_2H_5OH).

Is it just me, or does that model of ethanol look like a little doggie?

Make sure you know the properties of ionic compounds inside out and back to front. They may crop up in the exam.

Q1   Explain why calcium chloride, an ionic compound, has a high melting point.   [1 mark]

Covalent Bonding

These molecules might be <u>simple</u>, but you've still go to know about them. I know, the world is a cruel place.

Learn These Examples of Simple Molecular Substances

A <u>covalent bond</u> is a strong bond that forms when a <u>pair of electrons</u> is <u>shared</u> between two atoms. <u>Simple molecular substances</u> are made up of molecules containing a <u>few atoms</u> joined by <u>covalent bonds</u>. These <u>dot and cross diagrams</u> show six examples that you need to know about:

<u>Hydrogen, H_2</u>
Hydrogen atoms have <u>one electron</u>, so they need <u>one more</u> to complete the first shell. They can form a <u>single covalent bond</u> with another hydrogen atom to achieve this.

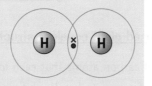

<u>Hydrogen Chloride, HCl</u>
This is very similar to H_2 — both atoms <u>only need</u> <u>one more electron</u> to complete their outer shells.

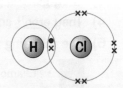

<u>Water, H_2O</u>
In <u>water molecules</u>, an oxygen atom shares a pair of electrons with two H atoms to form two <u>single covalent bonds</u>.

<u>Oxygen, O_2</u>
An oxygen atom needs <u>two more electrons</u> to complete its outer shell. In <u>oxygen gas</u>, each oxygen atom forms a <u>double covalent bond</u> (a bond made of <u>two shared electron pairs</u>) with another oxygen atom.

<u>Methane, CH_4</u>
Carbon has <u>four outer electrons</u>, which is <u>half</u> a full shell. It can form <u>four covalent bonds</u> with hydrogen atoms to fill up its outer shell.

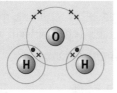

<u>Carbon dioxide, CO_2</u>
In <u>carbon dioxide molecules</u>, a carbon atom shares <u>two pairs of electrons</u> with two oxygen atoms to form two <u>double covalent bonds</u>.

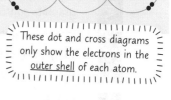

Simple molecules are tiny — they generally have sizes around 10^{-10} m. The <u>bonds</u> that form between these molecules are generally <u>about 10^{-10} m</u> too.

These dot and cross diagrams only show the electrons in the <u>outer shell</u> of each atom.

Properties of Simple Molecular Substances

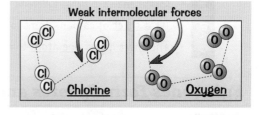

Weak intermolecular forces

<u>Chlorine</u>   <u>Oxygen</u>

1) Substances containing <u>covalent bonds</u> usually have <u>simple molecular structures</u>, like the examples above.

2) The atoms within the molecules are held together by <u>very strong covalent bonds</u>. By contrast, the forces of attraction <u>between</u> these molecules are <u>very weak</u>.

3) To melt or boil a simple molecular compound, you only need to break these <u>feeble intermolecular forces</u> and <u>not</u> the covalent bonds. So the melting and boiling points are <u>very low</u>, because the molecules are <u>easily parted</u> from each other.

4) Most molecular substances are <u>gases or liquids</u> at room temperature.

5) As molecules get <u>bigger</u>, the strength of the intermolecular forces <u>increases</u>, so <u>more energy</u> is needed to break them, and the melting and boiling points <u>increase</u>.

6) Molecular compounds <u>don't conduct electricity</u> because they don't contain any <u>free electrons</u> or <u>ions</u>.

7) There's no easy rule about solubility in water for simple molecules — some <u>are soluble</u> and some <u>aren't</u>.

Electrons £1,000,000

Polymers Are Made of Covalently Bonded Carbon Chains

1) <u>Polymers</u> are molecules made up of long chains of covalently bonded carbon atoms. A famous example is <u>poly(ethene)</u>.

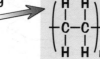

This is known as the repeat unit. The n shows that there's loads of these units joined, one after another.

2) They're formed when lots of small molecules called <u>monomers</u> join together (see pages 99–100).

May the intermolecular force be with you...

Remember, it's just the weak forces between molecules that are broken when a simple molecular substance melts.

Q1   Explain why oxygen, O_2, is a gas at room temperature.   [2 marks]

Q2   Explain why nitrogen, N_2, doesn't conduct electricity.   [1 mark]

Giant Covalent Structures and Fullerenes

Even more covalent structures for you to feast your eyes on... These ones are bigger, so they're better right?

Most Giant Covalent Structures Have Certain Properties

1) In giant covalent structures, all the atoms are bonded to each other by strong covalent bonds.

2) They have very high melting and boiling points as lots of energy is needed to break the covalent bonds.

3) They generally don't contain charged particles, so they don't conduct electricity.  Apart from graphite and graphene.

4) They aren't soluble in water.

5) The following examples are all carbon-based giant covalent structures.

DIAMOND
- Diamond is made up of a network of carbon atoms that each form four covalent bonds.
- The strong covalent bonds take lots of energy to break, so diamond has a high melting point.
- The strong covalent bonds also hold the atoms in a rigid lattice structure, making diamond really hard — it's used to strengthen cutting tools (e.g. saw teeth and drill bits).
- It doesn't conduct electricity because it has no free electrons or ions.

GRAPHITE
- In graphite, each carbon atom only forms three covalent bonds, creating sheets of carbon atoms arranged in hexagons.
- There aren't any covalent bonds between the layers — they're only held together weakly, so they're free to move over each other. This makes graphite soft and slippery, so it's ideal as a lubricating material.
- Graphite's got a high melting point — the covalent bonds in the layers need loads of energy to break.
- Only three out of each carbon's four outer electrons are used in bonds, so each carbon atom has one electron that's delocalised (free) and can move. So graphite conducts electricity and is often used to make electrodes.

GRAPHENE
- Graphene (a type of fullerene — see below) is one layer of graphite.
- It's a sheet of carbon atoms joined together in hexagons.
- The sheet is just one atom thick, making it a two-dimensional substance.

Fullerenes Form Spheres and Tubes

1) Fullerenes are molecules of carbon, shaped like closed tubes or hollow balls.

2) They're mainly made up of carbon atoms arranged in hexagons, but can also contain pentagons (rings of five carbons) or heptagons (rings of seven carbons).

3) Fullerenes can be used to 'cage' other molecules. The fullerene structure forms around another atom or molecule, which is then trapped inside. This could be used to deliver a drug directly to cells in the body.

4) Fullerenes have a huge surface area, so they could help make great industrial catalysts — individual catalyst molecules could be attached to the fullerenes (the bigger the surface area the better).

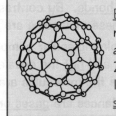
Buckminsterfullerene has the molecular formula C_{60} and forms a hollow sphere made up of 20 hexagons and 12 pentagons. It's a stable molecule that forms soft brownish-black crystals.

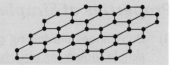 Catalysts speed up the rates of reactions without being used up (see page 82).

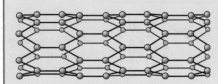
Nanotubes are also fullerenes. They are like tiny cylinders of graphene — so they conduct electricity. They also have a high tensile strength (they don't break when stretched) so can be used to strengthen materials without adding much weight. For example, they can be used to strengthen sports equipment that needs to be strong but also lightweight (e.g. tennis rackets).

Nanotubes — not to be confused with my Irish gran, Nan O'Brady...

Did you know that buckminsterfullerene is the state molecule of Texas? True story bro...

Q1 Give one use of graphite and state what property of graphite makes it suitable for this use. [2 marks]

Metallic Bonding

Ever wondered what makes <u>metals</u> tick? Well, either way, this is the page for you.

Metallic Bonding Involves Delocalised Electrons

1) <u>Metals</u> also consist of a <u>giant structure</u>.

2) The electrons in the <u>outer shell</u> of the metal atoms are <u>delocalised</u> (free to move around). There are strong forces of <u>electrostatic attraction</u> between the <u>positive metal ions</u> and the shared <u>negative electrons</u>.

3) These forces of attraction <u>hold</u> the <u>atoms</u> together in a <u>regular</u> structure and are known as <u>metallic bonding</u>. Metallic bonding is very <u>strong</u>.

4) Compounds that are held together by metallic bonding include metallic <u>elements</u> and <u>alloys</u> (see page 63).

5) It's the <u>delocalised electrons</u> in the metallic bonds which produce <u>all</u> the properties of metals.

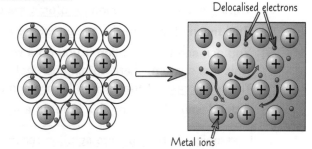

Delocalised electrons

Metal ions

Metals Have Certain Physical Properties

1) The electrostatic forces between the metal ions and the delocalised sea of electrons are very <u>strong</u>, so need <u>lots of energy</u> to be broken.

2) This means that most compounds with metallic bonds have very <u>high</u> melting and boiling points, so they're generally <u>shiny solids</u> at room temperature. They <u>aren't soluble</u> in water either.

3) Metals are also generally <u>more dense</u> than non-metals as the ions in the metallic structure are packed <u>close together</u>.

4) The <u>layers</u> of atoms in a pure metal can <u>slide over</u> each other (see page 63), making metals <u>malleable</u> — this means that they can be <u>hammered</u> or <u>rolled</u> into <u>flat sheets</u>.

5) The <u>delocalised electrons</u> carry electrical charge and thermal (heat) energy through the material, so metals are good <u>conductors</u> of <u>electricity</u> and <u>heat</u>.

Metals and Non-Metals Have Different Physical Properties

1) All metals have <u>metallic bonding</u> which causes them to have <u>similar</u> basic physical properties.

2) As non-metals <u>don't</u> have metallic bonding, they don't tend to exhibit the same properties as metals.

3) Non-metals form a variety of <u>different structures</u> so have a <u>wide range</u> of chemical and physical <u>properties</u>.

4) They tend to be <u>dull looking</u>, more <u>brittle</u>, have <u>lower boiling points</u> (they're not generally solids at room temperature), <u>don't</u> generally <u>conduct electricity</u> and often have a <u>lower density</u>.

5) Metals and non-metals also have <u>different chemical properties</u>. Non-metals tend to <u>gain electrons</u> to form full outer shells (they hang out on the top and right-hand side of the periodic table and their outer shells are generally <u>over half-filled</u>). Metals <u>lose electrons</u> to gain full outer shells (they're found at the bottom and left-hand side of the periodic table and their outer shells are generally <u>under half-filled</u>).

The blue boxes show the metals in the periodic table.

The white boxes show non-metals.

I saw a metal on the bus once — he was the conductor...

If your knowledge of metals is still feeling a bit delocalised, the questions below will help...

Q1   Copper is a metallic element. State what property of copper makes it suitable for using in electrical circuits and explain why it has this property.   [2 marks]

Q2   Thomas has samples of two solids, A and B. One of the samples is a metal. Solid A is shiny and conducts electricity as a solid. Solid B is a white powder that only conducts electricity when dissolved in water. Predict, with reasoning, whether solid A or solid B is likely to be the metal.   [3 marks]

Conservation of Mass

Being a diva, I prefer the conservation of sass. <u>Conservation of mass</u> is more useful in science exams though.

In a Chemical Reaction, Mass is Always Conserved

1) During a chemical reaction <u>no atoms are destroyed</u> and <u>no atoms are created</u>.

2) This means there are the <u>same number and types of atoms</u> on each side of a reaction equation.

3) You can see this in action if you do a reaction in a <u>closed system</u> (this is a system where nothing can get in or out). The <u>total mass</u> of the system before and after <u>doesn't change</u>.

4) A good way of showing this is to do a <u>precipitation</u> reaction. ◄

A precipitation reaction happens when two solutions react and an insoluble solid, called a precipitate, forms in the solution.

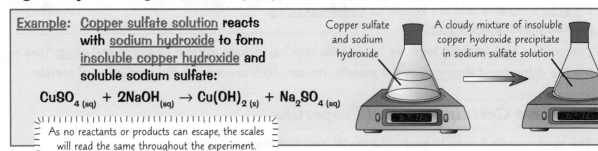

<u>Example:</u> <u>Copper sulfate solution</u> reacts with <u>sodium hydroxide</u> to form <u>insoluble copper hydroxide</u> and soluble sodium sulfate:

$$CuSO_{4 (aq)} + 2NaOH_{(aq)} \rightarrow Cu(OH)_{2 (s)} + Na_2SO_{4 (aq)}$$

Copper sulfate and sodium hydroxide

A cloudy mixture of insoluble copper hydroxide precipitate in sodium sulfate solution

As no reactants or products can escape, the scales will read the same throughout the experiment.

If the Mass Seems to Change, There's Usually a Gas Involved

In some experiments, you might observe a <u>change of mass</u> in an <u>unsealed reaction vessel</u> during a reaction. There are two reasons why this might happen:

1 If the mass <u>increases</u>, it's probably because at least one of the <u>reactants</u> is a <u>gas</u> that's found in air (e.g. oxygen) and the products are solids, liquids or aqueous.

- <u>Before</u> the reaction, the gas is floating around in the air. It's there, but it's not contained in the reaction vessel, so you <u>can't</u> measure its <u>mass</u>.

- When the gas <u>reacts</u> to form part of the <u>product</u>, it becomes contained inside the reaction vessel.

- So the total mass of the stuff <u>inside</u> the reaction vessel increases.

- For example, when a metal in an unsealed container reacts with oxygen from the air, the mass inside the container <u>increases</u>. The mass of the metal oxide produced equals the total mass of the <u>metal</u> and the <u>oxygen</u> that reacted from the air.
metal$_{(s)}$ + oxygen$_{(g)}$ → metal oxide$_{(s)}$

2 If the mass <u>decreases</u>, it's probably because some, or all, of the reactants are solids, liquids or aqueous and at least one of the <u>products</u> is a <u>gas</u>.

- <u>Before</u> the reaction, any solid, liquid or aqueous reactants are contained in the reaction vessel.

- If the vessel <u>isn't enclosed</u>, then the gas can <u>escape</u> from the reaction vessel as it's formed. It's no longer contained in the reaction vessel, so you <u>can't</u> measure its <u>mass</u>.

- So the total mass of the stuff <u>inside</u> the reaction vessel <u>decreases</u>.

- For example, when a metal carbonate thermally decomposes in an unsealed container to form a metal oxide and carbon dioxide gas, the mass of the container will appear to <u>decrease</u> as the carbon dioxide escapes. But in reality, the mass of the <u>metal oxide</u> and the <u>carbon dioxide</u> produced will equal the mass of the metal carbonate that reacted.
metal carbonate$_{(s)}$ → metal oxide$_{(s)}$ + carbon dioxide$_{(g)}$

A gas will expand to fill any container it's in. So if the reaction vessel isn't sealed the gas expands out from the vessel, and escapes into the air around. There's more about this on page 34.

Conservation of Mass — protecting mass for future generations...

Never, ever forget that, in a reaction, the total mass of reactants is the same as the total mass of products.

Q1 A student carries out the following reaction in an unsealed container: $2HCl_{(aq)} + Na_2S_{(aq)} \rightarrow H_2S_{(g)} + 2NaCl_{(aq)}$
Predict how the mass of the reaction vessel and its contents will change over the reaction. Explain your answer. [3 marks]

Relative Masses and Chemical Formulas

Time for some maths. "But this is chemistry, not maths," I hear you cry. "Tough cookies," I reply.

Relative Formula Mass, M_r — Easy Peasy

The relative formula mass, M_r, of a compound is the relative atomic masses (A_r) of all the atoms in its formula added together.

Look back at page 17 for more about relative atomic masses.

 **EXAMPLE:** Find the relative formula mass of:
a) magnesium chloride, $MgCl_2$,   b) calcium hydroxide, $Ca(OH)_2$.

 I have literally no idea what I'm doing.

a) Use the periodic table to find the relative atomic masses of magnesium and chlorine. Add up the relative atomic masses of all the atoms in the formula to get the relative formula mass.

$A_r(Mg) = 24$ $A_r(Cl) = 35.5$
$M_r(MgCl_2) = 24 + (2 \times 35.5)$
$= 24 + 71 = 95$

M_r of $MgCl_2 = 95$

b) The small number 2 after the bracket in the formula $Ca(OH)_2$ means that there's two of everything inside the brackets.

$A_r(Ca) = 40$ $A_r(O) = 16$ $A_r(H) = 1$
$M_r(Ca(OH)_2) = 40 + [(16 + 1) \times 2]$
$= 40 + 34 = 74$

M_r of $Ca(OH)_2 = 74$

The M_r of a compound is equal to the mass in grams of 1 mole (see next page) of the compound. So, 1 mole of magnesium chloride would weigh 95 g, and 1 mole of calcium hydroxide would weigh 74 g.

The Empirical Formula is the Simplest Ratio of Atoms

The empirical formula of a compound tells you the smallest whole number ratio of atoms in the compound.

 **EXAMPLE:** Find the empirical formula of glucose, $C_6H_{12}O_6$.

The numbers in the molecular formula of glucose are 6, 12 and 6.

To simplify the ratio, divide them by the largest number that goes into 6, 12 and 6 exactly — that's 6.

C: $6 \div 6 = 1$
H: $12 \div 6 = 2$
O: $6 \div 6 = 1$
The empirical formula of glucose is CH_2O.

You can use the empirical formula of a compound, together with its M_r, to find its molecular formula.

EXAMPLE: Compound X has the empirical formula C_2H_6N. The M_r of compound X is 88. Find the molecular formula of compound X.

1) Start by finding the M_r of the empirical formula. The A_r of carbon is 12, the A_r of hydrogen is 1 and the A_r of nitrogen is 14.

$M_r(C_2H_6N) = (2 \times A_r(C)) + (6 \times A_r(H)) + A_r(N)$
$= (2 \times 12) + (6 \times 1) + 14$
$= 24 + 6 + 14 = 44$

2) Divide the M_r of the compound by the M_r of the empirical formula.

$88 \div 44 = 2$

3) Now to get the molecular formula, you just multiply everything in the empirical formula by the result — in this case, by 2.

C: $2 \times 2 = 4$ H: $6 \times 2 = 12$ N: $1 \times 2 = 2$
The molecular formula of compound X is $C_4H_{12}N_2$.

This page is a relative masterpiece...

This stuff comes up a fair bit in chemistry, so make sure you've got to grips with it by doing loads of practice questions. Start with these. Use the periodic table on page 118 to find the A_r values you need.

Q1   Calculate the relative formula mass of ethanol, C_2H_5OH.   [1 mark]

Q2   What is the empirical formula of a compound with the molecular formula $C_4H_8Cl_2$?   [1 mark]

Moles

The mole might seem a bit confusing. I think it's the word that puts people off. But it's not that hard really...

"The Mole" is Simply the Name Given to a Certain Number of Particles

1) Just like <u>a million</u> is this many: 1 000 000, or <u>a billion</u> is this many: 1 000 000 000, a <u>mole</u> is an amount of particles (e.g. atoms, molecules or ions) equal to a number called <u>Avogadro's constant</u>, and it's this many: 602 000 000 000 000 000 000 000 or 6.02×10^{23}.

2) But why is Avogadro's constant useful? The answer is that when you get that number of atoms or molecules, <u>of any element or compound</u>, then, conveniently, they <u>weigh</u> exactly the same number of <u>grams</u> as the relative atomic mass, A_r (or relative formula mass, M_r) of the element or compound.

> One mole of atoms or molecules of any substance will have a mass in grams equal to the relative particle mass (A_r or M_r) for that substance.

Look back at page 27 if you've forgotten how to work out M_r.

Examples:

Carbon has an A_r of 12.   So one mole of carbon weighs exactly 12 g.

Nitrogen gas, N_2, has an M_r of 28 (2×14).   So one mole of nitrogen gas weighs exactly 28 g.

Hexane, C_6H_{14}, has an M_r of 86 ((6×12) + (14×1)).   So one mole of hexane weighs exactly 86 g.

So 12 g of carbon, 28 g of nitrogen gas and 86 g of hexane all contain the same number of particles, namely <u>one mole</u> or 6.02×10^{23} particles.

You Can Use Avogadro's Constant to Calculate Numbers of Particles

You need to be able to work out the <u>number</u> of <u>molecules</u>, <u>atoms</u> or <u>ions</u> in a certain number of <u>moles</u>.

EXAMPLE: How many atoms are there in 5 moles of oxygen gas?

1) Multiply <u>Avogadro's constant</u> by the number of moles you have to find the number of particles.

$6.02 \times 10^{23} \times 5 = 3.01 \times 10^{24}$

2) There are two atoms in each molecule of oxygen gas, so <u>multiply</u> your answer by 2.

$3.01 \times 10^{24} \times 2 = 6.02 \times 10^{24}$

Give your answer in standard form (in terms of $\times 10^x$) to save you having to write out lots of O's.

If you're asked for the number of particles in a given mass, you need to do a cheeky bit of converting first. There's a <u>nifty formula</u> you can use to find the number of moles in a certain mass of something.

$$\text{Number of Moles} = \frac{\text{Mass in g (of element or compound)}}{M_r \text{ (of compound) or } A_r \text{ (of element)}}$$

EXAMPLE: How many magnesium atoms are there in 60 g of magnesium? (A_r of Mg= 24)

1) Convert mass into moles using the equation.

moles = mass ÷ A_r
= 60 ÷ 24 = 2.5 moles

2) Multiply the number of moles by <u>Avogadro's constant</u> to find the number of atoms.

$6.02 \times 10^{23} \times 2.5$
= 1.505×10^{24}

If you need to get <u>from</u> a number of particles <u>to</u> a number of moles, you <u>divide</u> by 6.02×10^{23} instead.

What do moles do for fun? Moller skate...

Moles can give you a bit of a headache — so spend a bit of time getting your head round all this if you need to.

Q1   Calculate the number of moles in 90 g of water. M_r of water = 18.   [1 mark]

Q2   How many molecules of ammonia are present in 3.5 moles of ammonia gas?   [1 mark]

Q3   How many atoms are present in 81.4 g of calcium hydroxide, $Ca(OH)_2$? M_r of $Ca(OH)_2$ = 74.   [3 marks]

More Calculations

Holy moley. I hope you like <u>moles</u>, as we're about to get stuck into another page piled high with them. Make sure you've got to grips with everything on the last page before you embark on this one.

You Need to be Able to Rearrange the Equation for Moles

1) Just being able to plug numbers into the equation <u>moles = mass ÷ M_r</u> isn't going to cut it in the exams. Oh no... You need to be able to <u>rearrange</u> the formula to find out <u>other unknowns</u>, e.g. to find a mass if you've been given moles and M_r.

2) Putting an equation into a <u>formula triangle</u> makes rearranging equations straightforward. Here's the formula triangle that links moles, mass and relative formula mass.

3) To use a formula triangle, just cover the thing you want to find, and you're left with the expression you need to calculate it. The <u>line</u> through the triangle stands for <u>division</u>.

Or A_r

EXAMPLE:

How many moles are there in 66 g of carbon dioxide?

M_r of carbon dioxide (CO_2) = 12 + (16 × 2) = 44

moles = mass ÷ M_r = 66 ÷ 44 = 1.5 moles

EXAMPLE:

What mass of carbon is there in 4 moles of carbon dioxide?

mass = moles × A_r(C)
     = 4 × 12 = **48 g**

Concentration is a Measure of How Crowded Things Are

1) The <u>more solute</u> (the solid you're dissolving) you dissolve in a given volume, the <u>more crowded</u> the particles are and the <u>more concentrated</u> the solution.

2) Concentration can be measured in <u>grams per dm^3</u> ($g\ dm^{-3}$) — so 1 gram of stuff dissolved in 1 dm^3 of solution has a concentration of <u>1 $g\ dm^{-3}$</u>.

3) Here's the formula for finding <u>concentration</u> from the <u>mass of solute</u>:

1 dm^3
= 1 litre
= 1000 cm^3

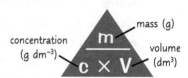

concentration = mass of solute ÷ volume of solution

EXAMPLE:

25 g of copper sulfate is dissolved in 500 cm^3 of water. What's the concentration in $g\ dm^{-3}$?

1) Make sure the values are in the <u>right units</u>. The mass is already in g, but you need to convert the volume to dm^3.

1000 cm^3 = 1 dm^3, so
500 cm^3 = (500 ÷ 1000) dm^3 = 0.5 dm^3

2) Now just substitute the values into the formula:

concentration = 25 ÷ 0.5 = **50 $g\ dm^{-3}$**

EXAMPLE:

What mass of sodium chloride is in 300 cm^3 of solution with a concentration of 12 $g\ dm^{-3}$?

1) Rearrange the formula so that mass is by itself.

mass = concentration × volume

2) Put the volume into the <u>right units</u>.

300 cm^3 = (300 ÷ 1000) dm^3 = 0.30 dm^3

3) Substitute the values into the rearranged formula.

mass = 12 × 0.30 = **3.6 g**

Concentration = mass of revision ÷ hours of good daytime TV...

None of the maths in these calculations is too hard. It's a bit of rearranging equations here and there, but apart from that, it's just some addition, multiplication and division — which is simple with a calculator in hand.

Q1 Calculate the mass of 0.200 moles of potassium bromide. M_r of KBr = 119 [1 mark]

Q2 0.500 moles of substance X has a mass of 87.0 g. What is the relative formula mass of X? [1 mark]

Q3 What mass of sodium hydroxide is contained in 200 cm^3 of a 55 $g\ dm^{-3}$ solution? [2 marks]

Topic 1 — Key Concepts in Chemistry

Calculating Empirical Formulas

You first met <u>empirical formulas</u> back on page 27, but now <u>they're back</u> and they mean business.

Empirical Formulas can be Calculated from Masses

You can work out the <u>empirical formula</u> of a compound from the masses of the elements it contains.

A sample of a hydrocarbon contains 36 g of carbon and 6 g of hydrogen. Work out the empirical formula of the hydrocarbon.

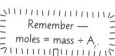
Remember — moles = mass ÷ A_r

1) First work out how many <u>moles</u> of each <u>element</u> you have.

A_r(C) = 12   moles of C = 36 ÷ 12 = 3 moles
A_r(H) = 1   moles of H = 6 ÷ 1 = 6 moles

2) Work out the <u>smallest whole number ratio</u> between the moles of C and H atoms to get the <u>empirical formula</u>.

Ratio C:H = 3:6. Now divide both numbers by the smallest — here it's 3. So, the ratio C:H = 1:2. The empirical formula must be CH_2.

You can also find the empirical formula of a compound from the percentage of each element it contains (its percentage composition). The method for doing this is the same as the one above, but you divide the percentage (rather than the mass) of each element by its A_r.

You can Use Experiments to Find Empirical Formulas

Here's an <u>experiment</u> you could use to calculate the empirical formula of a metal oxide, e.g. magnesium oxide.

1) Get a <u>crucible</u> and heat it until it's red hot. (This will make sure it's <u>clean</u> and there are no traces of <u>oil or water</u> lying around from a previous experiment.)

2) Leave the crucible to <u>cool</u>, then <u>weigh</u> it, along with its lid.

3) Add some clean <u>magnesium ribbon</u> to the crucible. <u>Reweigh</u> the crucible, lid and magnesium ribbon. The <u>mass of magnesium</u> you're using is this reading minus the initial reading for the mass of the crucible and lid.

4) <u>Heat</u> the crucible containing the magnesium. Put the lid on the crucible so as to <u>stop</u> any bits of solid from <u>escaping</u>, but leave a <u>small gap</u> to allow <u>oxygen</u> to enter the crucible.

5) Heat the crucible strongly for around <u>10 minutes</u>, or until all the magnesium ribbon has turned <u>white</u>.

6) Allow the crucible to <u>cool</u> and <u>reweigh</u> the crucible with the lid and its contents. The <u>mass</u> of <u>magnesium oxide</u> you have is this reading, minus the initial reading for the mass of the crucible and lid.

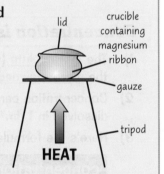
lid
crucible containing magnesium ribbon
gauze
tripod
HEAT

A student heats 1.08 g of magnesium ribbon in a crucible so it completely reacts to form magnesium oxide. The total mass of magnesium oxide formed was 1.80 g. Calculate the empirical formula of magnesium oxide.

1) The extra mass in the magnesium oxide must have come from oxygen, so you can work out the <u>mass of oxygen</u>.

mass of O = 1.80 − 1.08 = 0.72 g

2) Work out the <u>number of moles</u> of <u>magnesium</u> and <u>oxygen atoms</u> involved in the reaction.

moles of Mg = 1.08 ÷ 24 = 0.045 moles   moles of O = 0.72 ÷ 16 = 0.045 moles

3) Work out the <u>lowest whole number ratio</u> between Mg and O by dividing the moles of both by the <u>smallest number</u>.

Mg = 0.045 ÷ 0.045 = 1   O = 0.045 ÷ 0.045 = 1

This shows that the ratio between O and Mg in the formula is 1:1, so the empirical formula of the magnesium oxide must be MgO.

The empirical strikes back...

You may be given experimental results, like those in the example above, and asked to find the empirical formula of the compound formed. So read through the example thoroughly and make sure you can follow what's going on.

Q1   A 45.6 g sample of an oxide of nitrogen contains 13.9 g of nitrogen.
   What is the empirical formula of the nitrogen oxide?   [3 marks]

Limiting Reactants

Unlimited. Together we're unlimited. Unless you're a limiting reactant, in which case you're a big ol' limiter.

Reactions Stop When One Reactant is Used Up

1) A reaction stops when all of one of the reactants is used up. Any other reactants are said to be in excess.

2) The reactant that's used up in a reaction is called the limiting reactant (because it limits the amount of product that's formed).

3) The amount of product formed is directly proportional to the amount of the limiting reactant used. This is because if you add more of the limiting reactant there will be more reactant particles to take part in the reaction, which means more product particles are made (as long as the other reactants are in excess).

You can Calculate the Amount of Product from the Limiting Reactant

You can use a balanced chemical equation to work out the mass of product formed from a given mass of a limiting reactant. Here's how...

You could also use this method to find the mass of a reactant needed to produce a known mass of a product.

1) Write out the balanced equation.

2) Work out relative formula masses (M_r) of the reactant and product you're interested in.

3) Find out how many moles there are of the substance you know the mass of.

4) Use the balanced equation to work out how many moles there'll be of the other substance (i.e. how many moles of product will be made by this many moles of reactant).

5) Use the number of moles to calculate the mass.

EXAMPLE: Calculate the mass of aluminium oxide, Al_2O_3, formed when 135 g of aluminium is burned in air.

1) Write out the balanced equation: $4Al + 3O_2 \rightarrow 2Al_2O_3$

2) Calculate the relative formula masses of the reactants and products you're interested in.   Al: 27 Al_2O_3: $(2 \times 27) + (3 \times 16) = 102$

3) Calculate the number of moles of aluminium in 135 g: Moles = mass ÷ M_r = 135 ÷ 27 = 5

4) Look at the ratio of moles in the equation: 4 moles of Al react to produce 2 moles of Al_2O_3 — half the number of moles are produced. So 5 moles of Al will react to produce 2.5 moles of Al_2O_3.

5) Calculate the mass of 2.5 moles of aluminium oxide: mass = moles × M_r = 2.5 × 102 = **255 g**

EXAMPLE: Magnesium oxide, MgO, can be made by burning magnesium in air. What mass of magnesium is needed to make 100 g of magnesium oxide?

1) Write out the balanced equation. $2Mg + O_2 \rightarrow 2MgO$

2) Work out the relative formula masses of the reactants and products you're interested in.   Mg: 24   MgO: 24 + 16 = 40

3) Calculate the number of moles of magnesium oxide in 100 g: Moles = mass ÷ M_r = 100 ÷ 40 = 2.5

4) Look at the ratio of moles in the equation: 2 moles of MgO are made from 2 moles of Mg. So 2.5 moles of MgO will be formed from 2.5 moles of Mg.

5) Calculate the mass of 2.5 moles of Mg.   mass = moles × M_r = 2.5 × 24 = **60 g**

Relative mass — when you go to church with your parents...

A specially organically grown, hand-picked question for you, my dear. Don't say I don't spoil you.

Q1   Chlorine and potassium bromide react according to this equation: $Cl_2 + 2KBr \rightarrow Br_2 + 2KCl$
Calculate the mass of bromine produced when 23.8 g of
potassium bromide reacts with an excess of chlorine.

[4 marks]

Topic 1 — Key Concepts in Chemistry

Balancing Equations using Masses

You've already seen how to balance equations back on page 12. But, sometimes, you may have to balance equations given the masses of the reactants and products. Your good old friend the mole will come in handy...

You Can Balance Equations Using Reacting Masses

If you know the masses of the reactants and products that took part in a reaction, you can work out the balanced symbol equation for the reaction. Here are the steps you should take:

1) Divide the mass of each substance by its relative formula mass to find the number of moles.

> You may need to work out some unknown masses first (see below).

2) Divide the number of moles of each substance by the smallest number of moles in the reaction.

3) If needed, multiply all the numbers by the same amount to make them all whole numbers.

4) Write the balanced symbol equation for the reaction by putting these numbers in front of the formulas.

EXAMPLE:

Paula burns a metal, X, in oxygen. There is a single product, an oxide of the metal. Given that 25.4 g of X burns in 3.2 g of oxygen, write a balanced equation for this reaction. A_r of X = 63.5 and M_r of X oxide = 143.0.

1) Work out the mass of metal oxide produced. Because it's the only product, the mass of metal oxide produced must equal the total mass of reactants. $25.4 + 3.2 = 28.6$ g of X oxide

2) Divide the mass of each substance by its M_r or A_r to calculate how many moles of each substance reacted or were produced:

$$X: \frac{25.4}{63.5} = 0.40 \text{ mol} \quad O_2: \frac{3.2}{32.0} = 0.10 \text{ mol} \quad X \text{ oxide}: \frac{28.6}{143.0} = 0.20 \text{ mol}$$

3) Divide by the smallest number of moles, which is 0.10:

$$X: \frac{0.40}{0.10} = 4.0 \quad O_2: \frac{0.10}{0.10} = 1.0 \quad X \text{ oxide}: \frac{0.20}{0.10} = 2.0$$

4) The numbers are all whole numbers, so you can write out the balanced symbol equation straight away. $4X + O_2 \rightarrow 2(X \text{ oxide})$

5) The oxide of X must have a chemical formula containing X and O atoms. In order for the equation to balance, each molecule of X oxide must contain one O atom and 2 X atoms. $4X + O_2 \rightarrow 2X_2O$

You Can Work Out Limiting Reactants

EXAMPLE:

8.1 g of zinc oxide (ZnO) were put in a crucible with 0.30 g of carbon and heated until they reacted. Given that the balanced chemical equation for this reaction is: $2ZnO + C \rightarrow CO_2 + 2Zn$, work out the limiting reactant in this reaction.

1) Divide the mass of each substance by its M_r or A_r to find how many moles of each substance were reacted: $ZnO: \frac{8.1}{81} = 0.10 \text{ mol} \quad C: \frac{0.30}{12} = 0.025 \text{ mol}$

2) Divide by the smallest number of moles, which is 0.025: $ZnO: \frac{0.10}{0.025} = 4.0 \quad C: \frac{0.025}{0.025} = 1.0$

3) Compare the ratios between the moles of products with the balanced chemical equation. In the balanced equation, ZnO and C react in a ratio of 2 : 1. Using the masses, there is a 4 : 1 ratio of ZnO to C. So, ZnO is in excess, and C must be the limiting reactant.

What do moles have for pudding? Jam moly-poly...

The best way to get to grips with the maths on this page is by practising. Luckily for you, here's a question.

Q1 During an experiment, a student heats some iron, Fe, in the presence of an unknown gas, Y_2.
A single product forms, which is an ionic compound containing Fe and Y only.
Given that during the reaction, the student heated 17.92 g of iron, and 52.00 g of product were formed, write a balanced equation for the reaction. $A_r(Fe) = 56$, $M_r(\text{product}) = 162.5$ and $M_r(Y_2) = 71$ [5 marks]

Revision Questions for Topic 1

Phew. That's <u>Topic 1</u> over already. And I always say, the first topic is always, well sometimes, the hardest...
- Try these questions and <u>tick off each one</u> when you <u>get it right</u>.
- When you've done <u>all the questions</u> under a heading and are <u>completely happy</u> with it, tick it off.

Chemical Equations, Risks and Hazards (p.12-14) ☑

1) What are the chemicals on the left-hand side of a chemical equation called?
2) Write out the four state symbols used in chemical equations, and state what each one means.
3) Write out the formulas, complete with charges, of the carbonate and sulfate ions.
4) Sketch the following hazard symbols: a) toxic,   b) harmful.

Atoms, Isotopes and Electronic Configurations (p.15-19) ☑

5) Describe the main features of the plum pudding model of the atom.
6) Name the three subatomic particles found in an atom, and state the relative charge of each.
7) What can you say about the number of protons and electrons in a neutral atom?
8) What does the mass number tell you about an atom?
9) State what isotopes are, using an example to explain your answer.
10) Describe how Dmitri Mendeleev organised his version of the periodic table.
11) What can you say about the number of electron shells in elements in the same period?
12) What does the group number of an element in the periodic table tell you about its electronic structure?
13) How many electrons can fit into each of the first three electron shells?

Types of Bonding and Structures (p.20-25) ☑

14) What charge will the ion of a Group 6 element have?
15) Describe how ionic bonding occurs.
16) Draw a dot and cross diagram to show how magnesium chloride forms.
17) Why do ionic compounds conduct electricity when molten or in solution, but not as solids?
18) Outline the limitations associated with ball and stick models of molecules and compounds.
19) Draw a dot and cross diagram to show the bonding in a molecule of water.
20) Do simple molecular substances have high or low boiling points? Explain your answer.
21) Describe the structures of the following substances: a) diamond,   b) graphite.
22) Briefly describe what a fullerene is.
23) Give three general properties of metals.

Calculations and Moles (p.26-32) ☑

24) Why might the mass of an unsealed system increase during a chemical reaction?
25) Give a definition for the relative formula mass of a compound.
26) What is the empirical formula of a compound?
27) What equation links the number of moles with the mass and M_r of a substance?
28) What equation links the concentration of a solution with its volume and the mass of solute used?
29) Outline an experiment you could use to work out the empirical formula of magnesium oxide.
30) Explain what a limiting reactant is.
31) Describe how to balance an equation using the masses of the reactants and products in a reaction.

States of Matter

All stuff is made of <u>particles</u> (molecules, ions or atoms). The <u>forces</u> between these particles can be weak or strong, depending on whether it's a <u>solid</u>, <u>liquid</u> or a <u>gas</u>. Want to find out more? Then read on...

States of Matter Depend on the Forces Between Particles

1) There are <u>three states of matter</u> that you need to know about — <u>solids</u>, <u>liquids</u> and <u>gases</u>. You can model these three different states using the <u>particle model</u>.

2) In the particle model, each particle (it could be a molecule, an ion or an atom) is represented by a <u>solid sphere</u>.

3) The <u>properties</u> of each state of matter depend on the <u>forces</u> between the particles.

4) The forces between the particles can be <u>weak</u> or <u>strong</u>, depending on whether the substance is a solid, liquid or a gas.

The force is strong with this one.

SOLID

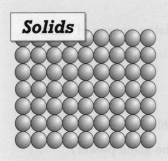

Solids

1) There are <u>strong forces</u> of attraction between particles, which hold them in <u>fixed positions</u> in a regular <u>lattice arrangement</u>.

2) The particles <u>don't move</u> from their positions, so all solids keep a <u>definite shape</u> and <u>volume</u>.

3) The particles in a solid <u>don't</u> have much <u>energy</u>.

4) They hardly move at all — in fact, they can only <u>vibrate</u> about their fixed positions. The <u>hotter</u> the solid becomes, the <u>more</u> they vibrate (causing solids to <u>expand</u> slightly when heated).

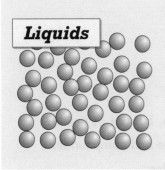

Liquids

1) There is <u>some force</u> of attraction between the particles. They're <u>free</u> to <u>move</u> past each other, but they do tend to <u>stick together</u>.

2) Liquids <u>don't</u> keep a <u>definite shape</u> and will flow to fill the bottom of a container. But they do keep the <u>same volume</u>.

3) For any given substance, in the <u>liquid state</u> its particles will have <u>more energy</u> than in the <u>solid state</u> (but <u>less</u> energy than in the <u>gas state</u>).

4) The particles are <u>constantly</u> moving with <u>random motion</u>. The <u>hotter</u> the liquid gets, the <u>faster</u> they move. This causes liquids to <u>expand</u> slightly when heated.

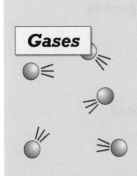

Gases

1) There's next to <u>no force</u> of attraction between the particles — they're <u>free</u> to <u>move</u>. They travel in <u>straight lines</u> and only interact when they <u>collide</u>.

2) Gases <u>don't</u> keep a definite <u>shape</u> or <u>volume</u> and will always <u>fill</u> any container. When particles bounce off the walls of a container they exert a <u>pressure</u> on the walls.

3) For any given substance, in the <u>gas state</u> its particles will have more energy that in the <u>solid state</u> or the <u>liquid state</u>.

4) The particles move <u>constantly</u> with <u>random motion</u>. The <u>hotter</u> the gas gets, the <u>faster</u> they move. Gases either <u>expand</u> when heated, or their <u>pressure increases</u>.

This means a gas will escape from a container if it isn't air-tight.

Don't ignore gases — they matter too...

Time to get to the bottom of the matter with all these states of matter. Try your hand at these questions...

Q1   Put the three states of matter, solid, liquid and gas, in order of the strength of the forces between their particles, starting with the weakest.   [1 mark]

Q2   Describe the arrangement of the particles and the forces between them in a gas.   [3 marks]

Changes of State

By <u>adding</u> or <u>taking away energy</u> from a substance, you can <u>convert</u> it from one <u>physical state</u> to another.

Heating or Cooling a Substance can Change its State

When a substance changes from one state of matter to another, it's a <u>physical change</u>. Physical changes are pretty easy to undo by <u>heating</u> or <u>cooling</u>.

> The red arrows show heat being added. The blue arrows show heat being given out.

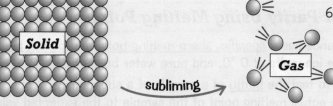

3) At a certain temperature, the particles have <u>enough energy</u> to <u>break</u> free from their positions. This is called <u>melting</u> and the solid turns into a <u>liquid</u>.

2) This makes the particles <u>vibrate more</u>, which <u>weakens</u> the <u>forces</u> that hold the solid together. This makes the solid <u>expand</u>.

1) When a <u>solid</u> is <u>heated</u>, its particles <u>gain</u> more <u>energy</u>.

4) When a liquid is <u>heated</u>, again the particles get even <u>more energy</u>.

5) This energy makes the particles <u>move faster</u>, which <u>weakens</u> and <u>breaks</u> the <u>bonds</u> holding the liquid together.

6) At a certain temperature, the particles have enough energy to <u>break</u> their <u>bonds</u>. This is called <u>evaporating</u> and the liquid turns into a <u>gas</u>.

Atoms are Rearranged During Chemical Reactions

1) <u>Chemical changes</u> are different to physical changes

2) Chemical changes happen during <u>chemical reactions</u>, when bonds between atoms break and the atoms <u>change places</u>. The atoms from the substances you <u>start off</u> with (the <u>reactants</u>) are rearranged to form <u>different substances</u> (the <u>products</u>).

3) Compared to physical changes, chemical changes are often <u>hard to reverse</u>.

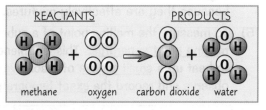

| REACTANTS | | PRODUCTS | |
| methane | oxygen | carbon dioxide | water |

Making Predictions about Substances from their Properties

You might be asked to <u>use data</u> to work out what <u>state</u> substances will be in under <u>certain conditions</u>.

EXAMPLE:

The table on the right gives information about the properties of four different substances.

Predict the state of substance D at 1000 °C.

Substance	Melting point / °C	Boiling point / °C
A	−218.4	−183.0
B	1535	2750
C	1410	2355
D	801	1413

1) The <u>melting point</u> of D is 801 °C and its <u>boiling point</u> is 1413 °C.

2) That means it's a solid <u>below 801 °C</u>, a gas <u>above 1413 °C</u>, and a liquid <u>in between</u>.

3) <u>1000 °C</u> is between 801 °C and 1413 °C, so... **D is a liquid at 1000 °C.**

I felt like changing state, so I moved from Texas to Michigan...

Predicting the state of something at a given temperature isn't too tricky. Best get some practice in anyway...

Q1   What states of matter are you moving from and to if you are condensing a substance?   [1 mark]

Q2   Using the table in the example above, predict the states of substances A, B and C at 1500 °C.   [3 marks]

Topic 2 — States of Matter and Mixtures

Purity

Purity — one of those special <u>science words</u> that has a special <u>science meaning</u> that doesn't quite match the everyday meaning that people use in real life... *sigh*...

Pure Substances Contain Only One Thing

1) In <u>everyday life</u>, the word '<u>pure</u>' is often used to mean 'clean' or 'natural'.

2) In <u>chemistry</u>, it's got a more <u>specific</u> meaning — a substance is <u>pure</u> if it's completely made up of a <u>single element or compound</u>.

3) If you've got <u>more than one</u> compound present, or different elements that aren't all part of a single compound, then you've got a <u>mixture</u>.

4) So, for example, <u>fresh air</u> might be thought of as nice and 'pure', but it's <u>chemically impure</u>, because it's a <u>mixture</u> of nitrogen, oxygen, argon, carbon dioxide, water vapour and various other gases.

5) Lots of <u>mixtures</u> are really <u>useful</u> — <u>alloys</u> (see page 63) are a great example. But sometimes chemists need to obtain a <u>pure sample</u> of a substance.

Having impure thoughts again, Henry?

You Can Test For Purity Using Melting Points

1) Every <u>pure</u> substance has a <u>specific, sharp melting point</u> and <u>boiling point</u>. For example, pure ice melts at 0 °C, and pure water boils at 100 °C.

2) You can use this to test the <u>purity</u> of a sample of a substance, by comparing the <u>actual</u> melting point of the sample to the <u>expected value</u>.

3) If a substance is a <u>mixture</u> then it will melt gradually over a <u>range of temperatures</u>, rather than having a <u>sharp</u> melting point, like a pure substance.

4) <u>Impure</u> substances will melt over a range of temperatures, because they are effectively mixtures.

5) To measure the melting point of a substance, you can use <u>melting point apparatus</u>. This is a piece of kit that allows you to heat up a <u>small sample</u> of a solid <u>very slowly</u>, so you can observe and record the <u>exact temperature</u> that it melts at.

> If you don't have melting point apparatus, you could use a water bath and a thermometer instead — but it's harder to control the temperature as exactly as when using this apparatus.

Example: Adil's teacher gives him samples of four <u>powdered solids</u>, labelled A, B, C and D. He uses <u>melting point apparatus</u> to determine the melting point of each of the solids. Adil's results are shown in the table below.

Solid	A	B	C	D
Melting point (°C)	82	72-79	101	63

Which of the four solids, A, B, C or D, was a mixture?

Answer: <u>B</u> — Adil's results show that solid B must be a <u>mixture</u>, because it melted over a <u>range of temperatures</u> (rather than melting at a specific temperature, as the other three solids did).

If in doubt, heat it up until it melts — that's my motto...

There are lots of ways to extract a pure substance out of a mixture. You'll learn about some over the next few pages.

Q1 Rachel buys a carton of juice labelled '100% pure orange juice'. Explain why the use of the word 'pure' on this label doesn't match the scientific definition. [2 marks]

Q2 Glyn is going to use melting point apparatus to test the melting point of a sample of pure benzoic acid. He says "I expect the sample to melt over a range of temperatures." Do you agree with Glyn? Explain your answer. [1 mark]

Distillation

Distillation is used to separate mixtures that contain <u>liquids</u>.
There are two types that you need to know about — <u>simple</u> and <u>fractional</u>.

Simple Distillation Separates Out Solutions

<u>Simple distillation</u> is used for separating out a <u>liquid</u> from a <u>solution</u>.
Here's how to use simple distillation to get <u>pure water</u> from <u>seawater</u>:

1) Pour your sample of seawater into the <u>distillation flask</u>.

2) Set up the <u>apparatus</u> as shown in the diagram. Connect the bottom end of the <u>condenser</u> to a cold tap using <u>rubber tubing</u>. Run <u>cold water</u> through the condenser to keep it cool.

3) Gradually heat the distillation flask. The part of the solution that has the lowest boiling point will <u>evaporate</u> — in this case, that's the water.

4) The water <u>vapour</u> passes into the condenser where it <u>cools</u> and <u>condenses</u> (turns back into a liquid). It then flows into the beaker where it is <u>collected</u>.

5) Eventually you'll end up with just the <u>salt</u> left in the flask.

The <u>problem</u> with simple distillation is that you can only use it to separate things with <u>very different</u> boiling points.

If you have a <u>mixture of liquids</u> with <u>similar boiling points</u>, you need another method to separate them out — like fractional distillation...

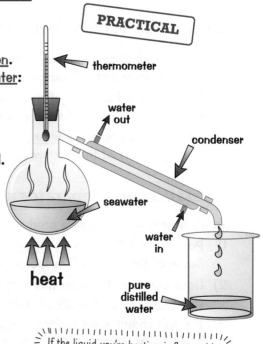

PRACTICAL

thermometer
water out
condenser
seawater
water in
heat
pure distilled water

If the liquid you're heating is flammable, use an electric heater or a water bath to heat it, rather than a Bunsen burner.

Fractional Distillation is Used to Separate a Mixture of Liquids

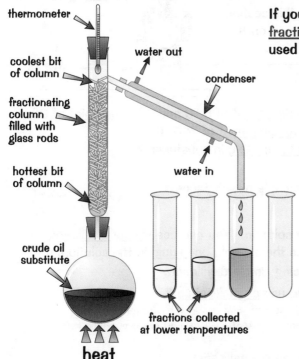

thermometer
water out
coolest bit of column
condenser
fractionating column filled with glass rods
hottest bit of column
water in
crude oil substitute
fractions collected at lower temperatures
heat

If you've got a <u>mixture of liquids</u> you can separate it using <u>fractional distillation</u>. Here's a lab demonstration that can be used to model <u>fractional distillation of crude oil</u> at a <u>refinery</u>:

1) Put your <u>mixture</u> in a flask. Attach a <u>fractionating column</u> and condenser above the flask as shown.

2) Gradually heat the flask. The <u>different liquids</u> will all have <u>different boiling points</u> — so they will evaporate at <u>different temperatures</u>.

3) The liquid with the <u>lowest boiling point</u> evaporates first. When the temperature on the thermometer matches the boiling point of this liquid, it will reach the <u>top</u> of the column.

4) Liquids with <u>higher boiling points</u> might also start to evaporate. But the column is <u>cooler</u> towards the <u>top</u>, so they will only get part of the way up before <u>condensing</u> and running back down towards the flask.

5) When the first liquid has been collected, <u>raise the temperature</u> until the <u>next one</u> reaches the top.

Fractionating — sounds a bit too much like maths to me...

The industrial method for fraction distillation of crude oil isn't quite as... well... crude as the one shown here.
If you're desperate to find out what goes on in oil refineries, have a look at page 87.

Q1   Propan-1-ol, methanol and ethanol have boiling points of 97 °C, 65 °C and 78 °C respectively.
A student uses fractional distillation to separate a mixture of these compounds.
State which liquid will be collected in the first fraction and explain why.   [2 marks]

Filtration and Crystallisation

If you've mixed a <u>solid</u> with a <u>liquid</u>, it should be pretty easy to <u>separate</u> them out again.
Which <u>method</u> you'll need to use depends on whether or not the solid can <u>dissolve</u> in the liquid.

Filtration is Used to Separate an Insoluble Solid from a Liquid

Filter paper folded into a cone shape.

The solid is left in the filter paper.

1) If the <u>product</u> of a reaction is an <u>insoluble solid</u>, you can use <u>filtration</u> to separate it out from the <u>liquid reaction mixture</u>.

2) It can be used in <u>purification</u> as well. For example, <u>solid impurities</u> can be separated out from a reaction mixture using <u>filtration</u>.

3) All you do is pop some <u>filter paper</u> into a <u>funnel</u> and pour your mixture into it. The liquid part of the mixture <u>runs through</u> the paper, leaving behind a <u>solid residue</u>.

Crystallisation Separates a Soluble Solid from a Solution

Here's how you <u>crystallise</u> a product...

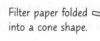

evaporating dish

1) Pour the solution into an <u>evaporating dish</u> and gently <u>heat</u> the solution. Some of the <u>water</u> will evaporate and the solution will get more <u>concentrated</u>.

2) Once some of the water has evaporated, <u>or</u> when you see crystals start to form (the <u>point of crystallisation</u>), remove the dish from the heat and leave the solution to <u>cool</u>.

3) The salt should start to form <u>crystals</u> as it becomes <u>insoluble</u> in the cold, highly concentrated solution.

4) <u>Filter</u> the crystals out of the solution, and leave them in a warm place to <u>dry</u>. You could also use a <u>drying oven</u> or a <u>desiccator</u> (a desiccator contains chemicals that remove water from the surroundings).

Choose the Right Purification Method

Choose wisely...

You might have to pick one of the <u>techniques</u> covered in this section to separate a mixture. The best technique to use will depend on the <u>properties</u> of the <u>substances</u> in the mixture.

<u>Example:</u>
A <u>mixture</u> is composed of two substances, X and Y.
<u>Substance X</u> is a <u>liquid</u> at room temperature, has a <u>melting point</u> of 5 °C and a <u>boiling point</u> of 60 °C.
<u>Substance Y</u> is a <u>solid</u> at room temperature. It has a <u>melting point</u> of 745 °C and a <u>boiling point</u> of 1218 °C. Substance Y <u>dissolves completely</u> in substance X.

Suggest a <u>purification method</u> you could use to obtain:
a) A pure sample of substance X,   b) A pure sample of substance Y.

<u>Answer:</u>

a) To get X on its own, you need to <u>distil it</u> from the solution. You can use <u>simple distillation</u> here — there's no need for fractional distillation as there's only <u>one liquid</u> in the solution.
You could obtain a pure sample of substance X using simple distillation.

b) To get a <u>soluble solid</u> out of a solution, you should use <u>crystallisation</u>.
In theory, if you <u>distilled</u> the mixture until all of substance X had evaporated off, you'd end up with just substance Y left in the flask. But there might be <u>traces</u> of substance X still hanging around — crystallisation's a better way of getting a <u>pure sample</u> of a solid from a solution.
You could obtain a pure sample of substance Y using crystallisation.

Its mum calls it Philliptration...

Some mixtures are made up of several components, so you might need to use a combination of the methods covered in this section to get all the different components out. I never said it was easy...

Q1   You are given a solution that has been made by dissolving copper sulfate crystals in water.
Describe a method that you could use to extract pure copper sulfate crystals from the solution.   [4 marks]

Chromatography

Chromatography is one analytical method that you need to know. It's all to do with a mobile phase and a stationary phase. But I'll tell you what, my revision's feeling in a stationary phase at the moment...

Chromatography uses Two Phases

Chromatography is a method used to separate a mixture of soluble substances and identify them. There are lots of different types of chromatography — but they all have two 'phases':

- A mobile phase — where the molecules can move. This is always a liquid or a gas.
- A stationary phase — where the molecules can't move. This can be a solid or a really thick liquid.

1) The components in the mixture separate out as the mobile phase moves over the stationary phase — they all end up in different places in the stationary phase.

2) This happens because each of the chemicals in a mixture will spend different amounts of time dissolved in the mobile phase and stuck to the stationary phase.

3) How fast a chemical moves through the stationary phase depends on how it 'distributes' itself between the two phases.

For each component in your mixture, you'll end up with one spot on your chromatogram (see next page for more on chromatograms).

In Paper Chromatography the Mobile Phase is a Solvent

In paper chromatography, the stationary phase is a piece of filter paper and the mobile phase is a solvent (e.g. water or ethanol).

Here's the method for setting it up:

PRACTICAL

1) Draw a line near the bottom of the paper — this is the baseline. (Use a pencil to do this — pencil marks are insoluble and won't move with the solvent as ink might.) Put a spot of the mixture to be separated on the line.

2) Put some of the solvent into a beaker. Dip the bottom of the paper (but not the spot) into the solvent.

3) Put a watch glass on the top of the beaker to stop any solvent from evaporating away.

4) The solvent will start to move up the paper. When the chemicals in the mixture dissolve in the solvent, they will move up the paper too.

5) You will see the different chemicals in the sample separate out, forming spots at different places on the paper.

(If one of your components is insoluble in the mobile phase, it won't move — it'll stay as a spot on the baseline.)

6) Remove the paper from the beaker before the solvent reaches the top. Mark the distance the solvent has moved (the solvent front) in pencil.

- watch glass
- solvent front
- paper
- spot of unknown substance
- point of origin
- solvent

If any substances in a mixture are insoluble in one solvent, you could try re-running the experiment with the same mixture, but using a different solvent. You may find this separates out the components, allowing you to find their R_f values (see next page).

The amount of time the molecules spend in each phase depends on two things:

- How soluble they are in the solvent.
- How attracted they are to the stationary phase.

Molecules with a higher solubility in the solvent (and which are less attracted to the paper) will spend more time in the mobile phase than the stationary phase — so they'll be carried further up the paper.

All hairdressers have to master Combatography...

Like a solvent working its way up some filter paper, let this chromatography stuff work its way into your brain...

Q1 In paper chromatography, what is the stationary phase? [1 mark]

Q2 A mixture of two chemicals, A and B, is separated using paper chromatography. Chemical A is more soluble in the solvent than B is. Which chemical, A or B, will end up closer to the solvent front? Explain your answer. [2 marks]

Interpreting Chromatograms

So, what use is chromatography, apart from making a pretty pattern of spots? Let's find out...

You can Calculate the R_f Value for Each Chemical

1) In paper chromatography, the piece of paper that you end up with is called a chromatogram.

2) If you know that you have chemicals in your mixture that are colourless (e.g. amino acids), you might have to spray the chromatogram with a chemical called a locating agent to show where the spots are.

3) You need to know how to work out the R_f values for the spots on a chromatogram.

4) An R_f value is the ratio between the distance travelled by the dissolved substance (the solute) and the distance travelled by the solvent. You can find R_f values using the formula:

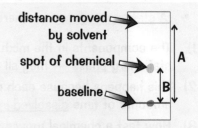

distance moved by solvent
spot of chemical
baseline
R_f value of this chemical = B ÷ A

$$R_f = \frac{\text{distance travelled by solute}}{\text{distance travelled by solvent}}$$

5) To find the distance travelled by the solute, measure from the baseline to the centre of the spot.

6) Chromatography is often carried out to see if a certain substance is present in a mixture. You run a pure sample of a substance that you think might be in your mixture alongside a sample of the mixture itself. If the sample has the same R_f values as one of the spots, they're likely to be the same.

7) Chemists sometimes run samples of pure substances called standard reference materials (SRMs) next to a mixture to check the identities of its components. SRMs have controlled concentrations and purities.

8) You can also use chromatography to do a purity test. A pure substance won't be separated by chromatography — it'll move as one blob (while a mixture should give you multiple blobs).

You can Combine Separation Techniques to Analyse Mixtures

PRACTICAL

Example: You could use a mixture of simple distillation and chromatography to analyse the composition of an ink.

1) Ink is a mixture of different dyes dissolved in a solvent.

2) To work out what solvent the ink contains, you could try doing a simple distillation. Simple distillation allows you to evaporate off the solvent and collect it — assuming that the solvent has the lowest boiling point of all substances in the ink, it will evaporate first.

3) The thermometer in the distillation set-up will read the boiling point of the solvent when it's evaporating (and therefore when it's being collected). You can use the boiling point of the solvent to try and determine what it is. For example, if the solvent in a certain ink evaporated at 100 °C, it would be quite likely to be water.

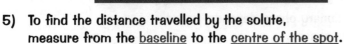

ink
heat   solvent

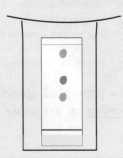

4) You could then carry out paper chromatography on a sample of the ink — this will separate out the different dyes in the ink, so that you can see how many there are.

5) You can compare the R_f values of the different spots on the chromatogram produced with reference values (or run further chromatography experiments with pure substances) to work out what dyes are in the ink.

For full details on how to run distillation and chromatography experiments, look back at pages 37 and 39.

J'aime la chromatographie... hmm, I think I need an interpreter...

You could be asked to work out R_f values in the exams, so make sure you know the formula in the purple box.

Q1 On a paper chromatogram, chemical X travelled 2.1 cm, chemical Y travelled 3.6 cm and the solvent front travelled 6.0 cm. Calculate the R_f value of chemical Y.   [2 marks]

Water Treatment

Water, water, everywhere... well, there is if you live in a submarine.

There are a Variety of Limited Water Resources in the UK

In the UK, there are a number of sources of water which can be purified to provide us
with potable water (water that is fit to drink). We get our water from:

1) SURFACE WATER: from lakes, rivers and reservoirs. In much of England
   and Wales, these sources start to run dry during the summer months.
2) GROUND WATER: from aquifers (rocks that trap water underground).
   In parts of south-east England, where surface water is very limited,
   as much as 70% of the domestic water supply comes from ground water.
3) WASTE WATER: from water that's been contaminated by a human process,
   e.g. as a by-product from some industrial processes. Treating waste water
   to make it potable is preferable to disposing of the water, which can be polluting.
   How easy waste water is to treat depends on the levels of contaminants in it.

Water is Purified in Water Treatment Plants

The water that comes out of your taps doesn't just come straight from the source — first it has to
be purified. How much purification it needs will depends on the source. Ground water from aquifers
is usually quite pure, but waste water and surface water needs a lot of treatment. But, wherever
it comes from, before we can drink it most water will be purified using the following processes:

1) Filtration — a wire mesh screens out large
   twigs etc., and then gravel and sand
   beds filter out any other solid bits.
2) Sedimentation — iron sulfate or aluminium
   sulfate is added to the water, which makes fine
   particles clump together and settle at the bottom.
3) Chlorination — chlorine gas is bubbled through
   to kill harmful bacteria and other microbes.

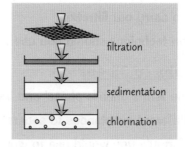

filtration

sedimentation

chlorination

Some soluble
impurities that are
dissolved in the water
are not removed as
they can't be filtered
out — these include
the minerals which
cause water hardness.

You Can Get Potable Water by Distilling Sea Water

1) In some very dry countries, e.g. Kuwait, sea water is distilled to produce drinking water.
2) Distillation needs loads of energy, so it's really expensive, especially if you're trying to produce large
   quantities of fresh water. So, we don't tend to use this method of producing potable water in the UK.

Water Used in Chemical Analysis must be Pure

1) Lots of chemistry involves carrying out experiments to work out what something is, or how it will react.
2) For experiments that involve mixing or dissolving something in water, you should use deionised water.
3) Deionised water is water that has had the ions (such as calcium,
   iron and copper ions) that are present in normal tap water removed.
4) These ions, although present in small amounts and harmless in tap water, can interfere
   with reactions. Using normal water could give your experiment a false result.

If water from the ground is ground water, why isn't rain sky water?

Ahhh... Every glass of tap water I drink tastes all the sweeter for knowing what it had to go through to get to me...

Q1   Outline how water is purified in a water treatment plant.   [3 marks]

Q2   A student plans to make a solution to use in an experiment by dissolving pure, solid sodium iodide
       in water. Suggest why the student should **not** use tap water. State what he should use instead.   [2 marks]

Revision Questions for Topic 2

Well, what a brilliant topic Topic 2 was. If I had to pick a favourite page, it would be all of them.
*   Try these questions and tick off each one when you get it right.
*   When you've done all the questions under a heading and are completely happy with it, tick it off.

States of Matter and Changes of State (p.34-35) ☑

1) Name the three states of matter. ☑
2) Describe the arrangement of particles, and the forces between them, in a solid. ☑
3) What happens to the forces between the particles in a solid as you melt it? ☑
4) What do you call the process of a substance changing from a liquid to a solid? ☑
5) Which are easier to reverse — chemical changes or physical changes? ☑

Purity (p.36) ☑

6) What is the chemical definition of purity? ☑
7) Explain why air isn't considered a pure substance, according to the scientific definition of pure. ☑
8) A substance melts over a range of temperatures. Is it likely to be a pure substance or a mixture? ☑

Separating Substances (p.37-38) ☑

9) Draw the apparatus you would use to carry out a simple distillation. ☑
10) What type of mixture would you separate using fractional distillation? ☑
11) Where is the hottest part of a fractionating column — at the top or at the bottom? ☑
12) Describe how to carry out filtration. ☑
13) What separation technique should you use to separate a soluble solid from a solution? ☑

Chromatography (p.39-40) ☑

14) Explain what the terms 'mobile phase' and 'stationary phase' mean in the context of chromatography. ☑
15) What causes different substances to separate out during a chromatography experiment? ☑
16) Write out the formula you would use to work out the R_f value of a substance from a chromatogram. ☑
17) How could you identify a substance from its R_f value? ☑

Water Treatment (p.41) ☑

18) Name three different sources of water that can be made potable. ☑
19) Name three processes that are used to make water potable. ☑
20) What is deionised water? ☑

Acids and Bases

Testing the pH of a solution means using an <u>indicator</u> — and that means pretty <u>colours</u>...

The pH Scale Goes From 0 to 14

1) The pH scale is a measure of <u>how acidic or alkaline</u> a solution is. A <u>neutral</u> substance has <u>pH 7</u>.

2) An <u>acid</u> is a substance with a <u>pH</u> of <u>less than 7</u>. Acids form <u>H$^+$ ions</u> in water.

3) The higher the <u>concentration of hydrogen ions</u> in a solution, the <u>more acidic</u> it is, so the lower its pH will be. In other words, as the concentration of hydrogen ions <u>increases</u>, the <u>pH decreases</u>.

4) A <u>base</u> is a substance that reacts with an acid to produce a <u>salt</u> and <u>water</u>.

5) An <u>alkali</u> is a base that is <u>soluble</u> in water. All alkalis have a <u>pH</u> of <u>more than 7</u> and they form <u>OH$^-$ ions</u> (otherwise known as <u>hydroxide ions</u>) in water.

6) In alkaline solutions, the higher the <u>concentration of OH$^-$ ions</u>, the higher the pH.

You Can Measure the pH of a Solution

1) An <u>indicator</u> is a <u>dye</u> that <u>changes colour</u> depending on whether it's <u>above or below a certain pH</u>.

2) Indicators are simple to use — <u>add a few drops</u> to the solution you're testing, then compare the colour the solution goes to a <u>pH chart</u> for that indicator. E.g. here's the pH chart for <u>Universal indicator</u>.

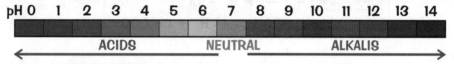

pH 0 1 2 3 4 5 6 7 8 9 10 11 12 13 14

ACIDS   NEUTRAL   ALKALIS

3) Some indicators that you need to know about are:

- litmus — is <u>red</u> in <u>acidic</u> solutions, <u>purple</u> in <u>neutral</u> solutions and <u>blue</u> in <u>alkaline</u> solutions.
- methyl orange — is <u>red</u> in <u>acidic solutions</u> and <u>yellow</u> in <u>neutral</u> and <u>alkaline</u> solutions
- phenolphthalein — is colourless in acidic or neutral solutions and <u>pink</u> in <u>alkaline</u> solutions.

Acids and Bases Neutralise Each Other

The reaction between an acid and a base is called <u>neutralisation</u>. It produces a <u>salt</u> and <u>water</u>.

$$HCl + NaOH \rightarrow NaCl + H_2O$$
acid   base   salt   water

Neutralisation reactions in <u>aqueous solution</u> can also be shown as an ionic equation (see p.13) in terms of <u>H$^+$</u> and <u>OH$^-$ ions</u>:

$$H^+_{(aq)} + OH^-_{(aq)} \rightarrow H_2O_{(l)}$$

When an acid neutralises a base (or vice versa), the <u>products</u> are <u>neutral</u>, i.e. they have a <u>pH of 7</u>. At pH 7, the concentration of hydrogen ions is <u>equal to</u> the concentration of hydroxide ions.

<u>Investigating the neutralisation reaction between calcium oxide (a base) and dilute hydrochloric acid.</u> **PRACTICAL**

1) Start by measuring out a set volume of <u>dilute hydrochloric acid</u> into a conical flask. Use a pipette or a measuring cylinder for this (see page 109).

2) Measure out a fixed mass of <u>calcium oxide</u> using a mass balance.

3) Add the calcium oxide to the hydrochloric acid.

4) Wait for the base to <u>completely react</u>, then record the <u>pH</u> of the solution, using either a pH probe (see page 110) or Universal indicator paper. (You can use a glass rod to spot samples of the solution onto the paper).

5) Repeat steps 2 to 4 until all the acid has reacted. You'll know you've reached this point when you get <u>unreacted</u> calcium oxide sitting at the bottom of the flask.

6) You can then plot a graph to see how <u>pH changes</u> with the mass of base added. You should find it looks a bit like this.

You can do this experiment with calcium hydroxide too.

When you first start adding base, the pH changes slowly...

...but there's a sudden change as you approach the point where the solution is neutral.

pH 14 12 10 8 6 4 2 0

amount of base added

This page should have all bases covered...

pHew, you got to the end of the page, so here's an interesting(ish) fact — your skin is slightly acidic (pH 5.5).

Q1   The pH of an unknown solution is found to be 2. Is the solution acidic or alkaline?   [1 mark]

Strong and Weak Acids

Right then. More on acids. Brace yourself...

Acids Produce Hydrogen Ions in Water

All acids can ionise (or dissociate) in solution — that means splitting up to produce a hydrogen ion, H^+, and another ion. For example,

$$HCl \rightarrow H^+ + Cl^-$$
$$HNO_3 \rightarrow H^+ + NO_3^-$$

HCl and HNO_3 don't produce hydrogen ions until they meet water.

Acids Can be Strong or Weak

1) Strong acids (e.g. sulfuric, hydrochloric and nitric acids) ionise almost completely in water, i.e. a large proportion of the acid molecules dissociate to release H^+ ions. They tend to have low pHs (pH 0-2).

2) Weak acids (e.g. ethanoic, citric and carbonic acids) do not fully ionise in solution, i.e. only a small proportion of the acid molecules dissociate to release H^+ ions. Their pHs tend to be around 2-6.

3) The ionisation of a weak acid is a reversible reaction, which sets up an equilibrium. Since only a few of the acid particles release H^+ ions, the equilibrium lies well to the left.

Strong acid: $HCl \longrightarrow H^+ + Cl^-$

Weak acid: $CH_3COOH \rightleftharpoons H^+ + CH_3COO^-$

For more on equilibria turn to page 59.

Don't Confuse Strong Acids with Concentrated Acids

1) Acid strength (i.e. strong or weak) tells you what proportion of the acid molecules ionise in water.

2) The concentration of an acid is different. Concentration measures how much acid there is in a litre (1 dm³) of water. Concentration is basically how watered down your acid is.

3) An acid with a large number of acid molecules compared to the volume of water is said to be concentrated. An acid with a small number of acid molecules compared to the volume of water is said to be dilute.

Concentration is measured in g dm⁻³ or mol dm⁻³.

4) Note that concentration describes the total number of dissolved acid molecules — not the number of molecules that produce hydrogen ions.

5) The more grams (or moles) of acid per dm³, the more concentrated the acid is.

6) So you can have a dilute strong acid, or a concentrated weak acid.

Changing the Concentration of an Acid Affects its pH

If the concentration of H^+ ions increases by a factor of 10, the pH decreases by 1. So if the H^+ ion concentration increases by a factor of 100 (= 10 × 10), the pH decreases by 2 (= 1 + 1), and so on. Decreasing the H^+ ion concentration has the opposite effect — a decrease by a factor of 10 in the H^+ concentration means an increase of 1 on the pH scale.

EXAMPLE:

A solution with a hydrogen ion concentration of 0.001 mol/dm³ has a pH of 3. What would happen to the pH if you increased the hydrogen ion concentration to 0.01 mol/dm³?

The H^+ concentration has increased by a factor of 10, so the pH would decrease by 1. So the new pH would be 3 − 1 = 2.

Weak acid or strong acid? I know which goes better with chips...

Acids are acidic because of H^+ ions. And strong acids are strong because they let go of all their H^+ ions at the drop of a hat... Well, at the drop of a drop of water.

Q1   Explain the difference between a strong acid and a weak acid.   [2 marks]

Q2   A student added a strong acid to a solution with a pH of 6. The new solution had a pH of 3. State whether the concentration of H^+ had increased or decreased and by what factor.   [2 marks]

Reactions of Acids

You met bases, back on page 43. You've also seen how they react with acids in <u>neutralisation reactions</u> to form a <u>salt</u> and <u>water</u>. So I'm sure you'll be overjoyed to hear there are more of these reactions coming up.

Salts Form When Acids React with Bases

1) A <u>salt</u> is formed during a <u>neutralisation reaction</u> (a reaction between an <u>acid</u> and a <u>base</u>). <u>Salts</u> are ionic compounds.

2) In general, <u>hydrochloric acid</u> produces <u>chloride</u> salts, <u>sulfuric acid</u> produces <u>sulfate salts</u> and <u>nitric acid</u> produces <u>nitrate salts</u>.

3) You need to be able to remember what happens when you add acids to various bases...

Acid + Metal Oxide → Salt + Water

Examples: $2HCl + CuO \rightarrow CuCl_2 + H_2O$ (Copper chloride)
$H_2SO_4 + ZnO \rightarrow ZnSO_4 + H_2O$ (Zinc sulfate)
$2HNO_3 + MgO \rightarrow Mg(NO_3)_2 + H_2O$ (Magnesium nitrate)

Acid + Metal Hydroxide → Salt + Water

Examples: $HCl + NaOH \rightarrow NaCl + H_2O$ (Sodium chloride)
$H_2SO_4 + Zn(OH)_2 \rightarrow ZnSO_4 + 2H_2O$ (Zinc sulfate)
$HNO_3 + KOH \rightarrow KNO_3 + H_2O$ (Potassium nitrate)

These are the same as the acid/alkali neutralisation reaction you met on page 43.

Salts Also Form When Acids React With Metals or Metal Carbonates

You also need to know what happens when you react an <u>acid</u> with a <u>metal</u> or a <u>metal carbonate</u>:

Acid + Metal → Salt + Hydrogen

Examples: $2HCl + Mg \rightarrow MgCl_2 + H_2$ (Magnesium chloride)
$H_2SO_4 + Mg \rightarrow MgSO_4 + H_2$ (Magnesium sulfate)

The reaction of nitric acid with metals can be more complicated — you get a nitrate salt, but instead of hydrogen gas, the other products are usually a mixture of water, NO and NO_2.

1) You can <u>test for hydrogen</u> using a lighted splint.
2) Hydrogen makes a "<u>squeaky pop</u>" with a <u>lighted splint</u>.
3) The noise comes from the <u>hydrogen burning</u> with the <u>oxygen</u> in the air to form water.

hydrogen

squeaky pop!

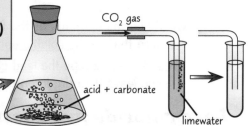

♪ Eeeee! ♪

Acid + Metal Carbonate → Salt + Water + Carbon Dioxide

Examples:

$2HCl + Na_2CO_3 \rightarrow 2NaCl + H_2O + CO_2$ (Sodium chloride)
$H_2SO_4 + K_2CO_3 \rightarrow K_2SO_4 + H_2O + CO_2$ (Potassium sulfate)
$2HNO_3 + ZnCO_3 \rightarrow Zn(NO_3)_2 + H_2O + CO_2$ (Zinc nitrate)

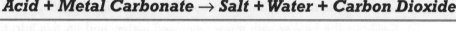

CO_2 gas

acid + carbonate

limewater

1) You can test to see if a gas is <u>carbon dioxide</u> by bubbling it through <u>limewater</u>.
2) If the gas is carbon dioxide, the limewater will <u>turn cloudy</u>.

Nitrates — much cheaper than day-rates...

What a lot of reactions. Better take a peek back at page 12 for help with writing and balancing chemical equations.

Q1   Write a balanced chemical equation for the reaction of hydrochloric acid with calcium carbonate.   [2 marks]

Making Insoluble Salts

Unfortunately for you, you've got to learn which salts are <u>soluble</u> and which ones <u>aren't</u>. Tough luck...

The Rules of Solubility

Soluble things dissolve in water. Insoluble things don't.

1) How you make a salt depends on whether it's <u>soluble</u> or <u>insoluble</u>.

2) You may need to work out if, when two solutions are mixed, a salt will form as a <u>precipitate</u> (i.e. it's an insoluble salt), or whether it will just form <u>in solution</u> (i.e. it's a soluble salt).

3) This table is a pretty fail-safe way of working out whether a substance is soluble in water or not.

Substance	Soluble or Insoluble?
common salts of sodium, potassium and ammonium	soluble
nitrates	soluble
common chlorides	soluble (except silver chloride and lead chloride)
common sulfates	soluble (except lead, barium and calcium sulfate)
common carbonates and hydroxides	insoluble (except for sodium, potassium and ammonium ones)

Making Insoluble Salts — Precipitation Reactions

1) To make a pure, dry sample of an <u>insoluble</u> salt, you can use a <u>precipitation reaction</u>. You just need to pick the right two <u>soluble salts</u> and <u>react</u> them together to get your <u>insoluble salt</u>.

2) E.g. to make <u>lead chloride</u> (insoluble), mix <u>lead nitrate</u> and <u>sodium chloride</u> (both soluble).

lead nitrate + sodium chloride → lead chloride + sodium nitrate

$$Pb(NO_3)_{2\ (aq)} + 2NaCl_{(aq)} \rightarrow PbCl_{2\ (s)} + 2NaNO_{3\ (aq)}$$

Method

1) Add 1 spatula of <u>lead nitrate</u> to a test tube. Add <u>water</u> to dissolve it. You should use deionised water to make sure there are no other ions about. <u>Shake it thoroughly</u> to ensure that all the lead nitrate has <u>dissolved</u>. Then, in a separate test tube, do the same with 1 spatula of <u>sodium chloride</u>.

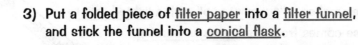

precipitate

2) Tip the <u>two solutions</u> into a small beaker, and give it a good stir to make sure it's all mixed together. The lead chloride should <u>precipitate</u> out.

3) Put a folded piece of <u>filter paper</u> into a <u>filter funnel</u>, and stick the funnel into a <u>conical flask</u>.

filter paper

filter funnel

4) <u>Pour</u> the contents of the beaker into the middle of the filter paper. Make sure that the solution doesn't go above the filter paper — otherwise some of the solid could dribble down the side.

5) <u>Swill out</u> the beaker with more deionised water, and tip this into the filter paper — to make sure you get <u>all the precipitate</u> from the beaker.

6) Rinse the contents of the filter paper with deionised water to make sure that <u>all the soluble sodium nitrate</u> has been washed away.

lead chloride

7) Then just scrape the <u>lead chloride</u> onto fresh filter paper and leave it to dry in an oven or a desiccator.

Lead chloride just doesn't behave — it's an intolerable salt...

The theory may seem dull, but you'll probably get to make some nice salts in your class, and that's pretty cool.

Q1 State whether the following salts are soluble or insoluble:
a) potassium chloride   b) copper carbonate   c) calcium sulfate   d) ammonium hydroxide [4 marks]

Q2 Suggest two reactants you could use to form barium sulfate in a precipitation reaction. [2 marks]

Making Soluble Salts

You met the technique for making <u>insoluble salts</u> on the last page. Time for <u>soluble salts</u> now...

Making Soluble Salts — Use an Acid and an Insoluble Base

PRACTICAL

1) You can make a <u>soluble salt</u> by reacting an <u>acid</u> that contains one of the ions you want in the salt with an <u>insoluble base</u> that contains the other ion you need (often a <u>metal oxide</u> or <u>metal hydroxide</u>).

For some salts, you can use a <u>metal</u> instead of the base.

2) Start by <u>heating the acid</u> in a <u>water bath</u> (see p.112) — this speeds up the reaction between the acid and the insoluble base. Do this in a <u>fume cupboard</u> to avoid releasing acid fumes into the room.

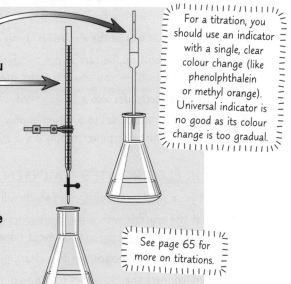

filter paper
filter funnel
excess solid
salt and water

3) Then add the <u>base</u> to the <u>acid</u> — the base and acid will react to produce a <u>soluble salt</u> (and water). You will know when the base is in excess and all the acid has been neutralised because the excess solid will just <u>sink</u> to the bottom of the flask.

(It's important that the base is in excess so that you don't have any leftover acid in your product.)

4) <u>Filter</u> off the <u>excess</u> solid to get a solution containing only the <u>salt</u> and <u>water</u>.

5) <u>Heat the solution gently</u>, using a Bunsen burner, to slowly <u>evaporate</u> off some of the water. Leave the solution to cool and allow the salt to <u>crystallise</u> (see p.38). Filter off the <u>solid salt</u> and leave it to <u>dry</u>.

> <u>Example:</u> You can add <u>copper oxide</u> to warm <u>sulfuric acid</u> to make a solution of <u>copper sulfate</u>:
>
> $$CuO_{(s)} + H_2SO_{4\,(aq)} \rightarrow CuSO_{4\,(aq)} + H_2O_{(l)}$$
>
> If you evaporate off some of the water and leave this solution to <u>crystallise</u>, you should get lovely <u>blue crystals</u> of <u>hydrated copper sulfate</u>, which you can <u>filter off</u> and <u>dry</u>.

You can Make Soluble Salts Using Acid/Alkali Reactions

1) Soluble salts (salts that dissolve in water) can be made by reacting an acid with an <u>alkali</u>.

2) But you can't tell whether the reaction has <u>finished</u> — there's no signal that all the acid has been neutralised. You also can't just add an <u>excess</u> of alkali to the acid, because the salt is <u>soluble</u> and would be contaminated with the excess alkali.

3) Instead, you need to work out <u>exactly</u> the right amount of alkali to <u>neutralise</u> the acid. For this, you need to do a <u>titration</u> using an <u>indicator</u>. Here's what you do...

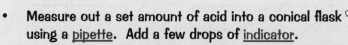

- Measure out a set amount of acid into a conical flask using a <u>pipette</u>. Add a few drops of <u>indicator</u>.

- Slowly add alkali to the acid, using a <u>burette</u>, until you reach the <u>end point</u> — this is when the acid's been exactly neutralised and the indicator <u>changes colour</u>.

- Then, carry out the reaction using exactly the same volumes of alkali and acid but with no <u>indicator</u>, so the salt <u>won't be contaminated</u> with indicator.

- The <u>solution</u> that remains when the reaction is complete contains only the <u>salt</u> and <u>water</u>.

- Slowly <u>evaporate</u> off some of the water and then leave the solution to crystallise (see page 38 for more on crystallisation). Filter off the solid and dry it — you'll be left with a <u>pure</u>, <u>dry</u> salt.

For a titration, you should use an indicator with a single, clear colour change (like phenolphthalein or methyl orange). Universal indicator is no good as its colour change is too gradual.

See page 65 for more on titrations.

I was attacked by a nasty copper sulfate — it was a-salt...

Yet more salts for you to make. If I were you though, I'd just get my salts from a sachet at the local chippy...

Q1   Iron nitrate is a soluble salt that can be made from iron oxide (an insoluble base) and nitric acid. Suggest a method you could use to make a pure sample of iron nitrate from these reactants.   [5 marks]

Electrolysis

Now I hope you're sitting comfortably. We're about to embark on three pages on <u>electrolysis</u>. What a treat.

Electrolysis Involves Oxidation and Reduction

1) <u>Electrolysis</u> is the <u>breaking down</u> of a substance using <u>electricity</u>. An electric current is passed through an <u>electrolyte</u> (a <u>molten</u> or <u>dissolved</u> ionic compound), causing it to <u>decompose</u>.

See page 54 for more on oxidation and reduction.

2) In electrolysis, <u>oxidation</u> (<u>loss of electrons</u>) and <u>reduction</u> (<u>gain of electrons</u>) occur.

3) The <u>positive ions</u> (<u>cations</u>) in the electrolyte move towards the <u>cathode</u> (negative electrode) and are reduced (<u>gain</u> electrons).

4) The <u>negative ions</u> (<u>anions</u>) in the electrolyte move towards the <u>anode</u> (positive electrode) and are oxidised (<u>lose</u> electrons).

This creates a flow of charge through the electrolyte.

5) As ions gain or lose electrons they form the uncharged substances and are <u>discharged</u> from the electrolyte.

<u>Half equations</u> show how electrons are transferred during reactions. They're really useful for showing what happens at <u>each electrode</u> during electrolysis. To write a half equation:

1) Put <u>one</u> of the things <u>being oxidised or reduced</u> on one side of an arrow, and the thing it gets <u>oxidised or reduced to</u> on the other.

2) Balance up the <u>numbers of atoms</u> just like in a normal equation.

3) Then add <u>electrons</u> (written $\underline{e^-}$) on to one side to balance up the charges.

The charges on each side of the equation should balance.

<u>Examples</u>: Sodium is losing one electron to become a sodium ion: $Na \rightarrow Na^+ + e^-$

Hydrogen ions are gaining electrons to become hydrogen: $2H^+ + 2e^- \rightarrow H_2$

Here's How to Set Up an Electrochemical Cell

1) An <u>electrochemical cell</u> is a <u>circuit</u>, made up of the anode, cathode, electrolyte, a power source and the wires that connect the two electrodes.

2) You need to know how to <u>set up</u> an electrochemical cell. The method used depends on whether your electrolyte is a <u>solution</u> or a <u>molten ionic substance</u>.

You could put an ammeter or bulb in series with your circuit to check you've set it up correctly.

IF YOUR ELECTROLYTE'S A SOLUTION

1) Get <u>two inert</u> (unreactive) <u>electrodes</u>, e.g. graphite or platinum electrodes.

2) Clean the surfaces of the electrodes using some <u>emery paper</u> (or sandpaper).

3) From this point on, be careful <u>not to touch</u> the surfaces of the electrodes with your hands — you could transfer grease back onto the strips.

4) Place both electrodes into a <u>beaker</u> filled with your <u>electrolyte</u>.

5) Connect the electrodes to a power supply using <u>crocodile clips</u> and <u>wires</u>. When you turn the power supply on, a <u>current</u> will flow through the cell.

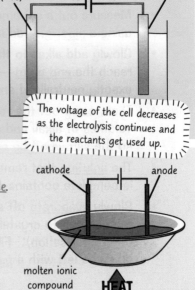

cathode (−ve)   d.c. power supply −ve +ve   anode (+ve)

The voltage of the cell decreases as the electrolysis continues and the reactants get used up.

IF YOUR ELECTROLYTE'S A MOLTEN IONIC SUBSTANCE

1) Put your <u>solid ionic substance</u> (which will become your electrolyte) in a <u>crucible</u>.

2) Heat the crucible with a <u>Bunsen burner</u> until the <u>solid's molten</u>. You should do this in a <u>fume cupboard</u> to avoid releasing any toxic fumes into the room.

3) Once the solid's molten, dip two clean, <u>inert electrodes</u> into the electrolyte.

4) Then, connect the <u>electrodes</u> to a <u>power supply</u> using wires and clips — you should get a <u>current</u> flowing through the cell when you turn the power on.

cathode   anode

molten ionic compound   **HEAT**

Two electrodes and a lake of fire — electrochemical hell...

You can also do electrolysis with non-inert electrodes. Have a look at page 50 for more about this.

Q1   At which electrode does oxidation happen during electrolysis?   [1 mark]

Topic 3 — Chemical Changes

Predicting Products of Electrolysis

This stuff is electrifying. You'll be on the edge of your seat with all this fun, fun, fun <u>electrolysis</u>.

In Molten Ionic Solids, There's Only One Source of Ions

1) An <u>ionic solid can't</u> be electrolysed because the ions are in fixed positions and <u>can't move</u>.

2) <u>Molten ionic compounds can</u> be electrolysed because the ions can <u>move freely</u> and conduct electricity.

3) Positive <u>metal ions</u> are <u>reduced</u> to <u>metal atoms</u> at the cathode.

4) Negative <u>ions</u> are <u>oxidised</u> to atoms or molecules at the <u>anode</u>.

5) In the example of $PbBr_2$, you'd see a <u>brown vapour</u> of bromine gas at the anode and a silver coloured liquid at the cathode as <u>molten lead</u> is formed.

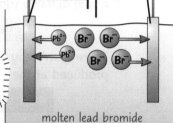

cathode (−ve)   anode (+ve)

molten lead bromide

$$Pb^{2+} + 2e^- \rightarrow Pb \qquad 2Br^- \rightarrow Br_2 + 2e^-$$

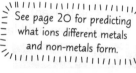
See page 20 for predicting what ions different metals and non-metals form.

6) It's easy to predict what products you get when you electrolyse <u>molten</u> substances — but you need to get the <u>half equations</u> (see p.48) right too. Here are some examples:

Molten Electrolyte	Product at Cathode	Half equation at Cathode	Product at Anode	Half equation at Anode
potassium chloride, KCl	potassium	$K^+ + e^- \rightarrow K$	chlorine	$2Cl^- \rightarrow Cl_2 + 2e^-$
aluminium oxide, Al_2O_3	aluminium	$Al^{3+} + 3e^- \rightarrow Al$	oxygen	$2O^{2-} \rightarrow O_2 + 4e^-$

Electrolysis of Aqueous Solutions is a Bit More Complicated

1) In <u>aqueous solutions</u>, as well as the <u>ions</u> from the ionic compound, there will be <u>hydrogen ions</u> (H^+) and <u>hydroxide ions</u> (OH^-) from the <u>water</u>: $H_2O_{(l)} \rightleftharpoons H^+_{(aq)} + OH^-_{(aq)}$

2) At the <u>cathode</u>, if H^+ ions and metal ions are present, <u>hydrogen gas</u> will be produced if the metal is <u>more reactive</u> than hydrogen (e.g. sodium). If the metal is <u>less reactive</u> than hydrogen (e.g. copper or silver), then a solid layer of the <u>pure metal</u> will be produced instead.

You can use reactivity series to find out which metals are more or less reactive than hydrogen (see page 52).

3) At the <u>anode</u>, if <u>OH^- and halide ions</u> (Cl^-, Br^-, I^-) are present, molecules of chlorine, bromine or iodine will be formed. If <u>no halide ions</u> are present, then <u>oxygen</u> will be formed.

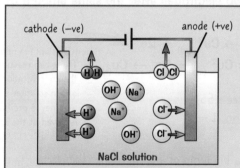

cathode (−ve)   anode (+ve)

NaCl solution

A solution of <u>sodium chloride</u> (NaCl) contains <u>four different ions</u>: Na^+, Cl^-, OH^- and H^+.

- <u>Sodium</u> metal is more reactive than hydrogen. So at the cathode, <u>hydrogen gas</u> is produced.

$$2H^+ + 2e^- \rightarrow H_2$$

- <u>Chloride ions</u> are present in the solution. So at the anode, <u>chlorine gas</u> is produced.

$$2Cl^- \rightarrow Cl_2 + 2e^-$$

Sir Chlo Ride

Sir Chlo Rode

Aqueous Electrolyte	Product at Cathode	Half equation at Cathode	Product at Anode	Half equation at Anode
copper chloride, $CuCl_2$	copper	$Cu^{2+} + 2e^- \rightarrow Cu$	chlorine	$2Cl^- \rightarrow Cl_2 + 2e^-$
sodium sulfate, Na_2SO_4	hydrogen	$2H^+ + 2e^- \rightarrow H_2$	oxygen	$4OH^- \rightarrow O_2 + 2H_2O + 4e^-$
water acidified with sulfuric acid, H_2O/H_2SO_4	hydrogen	$2H^+ + 2e^- \rightarrow H_2$	oxygen	$4OH^- \rightarrow O_2 + 2H_2O + 4e^-$

Faster shopping at the supermarket — use Electrolleys...

So it's kinda confusing this electrolysis malarkey — you need to take it slow and make sure you get it.

Q1   An aqueous solution of copper bromide, $CuBr_2$, is electrolysed using inert electrodes. Give the half equation to show the reaction occurring at the anode.

[2 marks]

Electrolysis of Copper Sulfate

The products you get from electrolysis depend not only on your <u>electrolyte</u>, but also on your <u>electrodes</u> too...

Electrolysis of Copper Sulfate with Inert Electrodes Produces Oxygen

1) A solution of <u>copper sulfate</u> ($CuSO_4$) contains <u>four different ions</u>: Cu^{2+}, SO_4^{2-}, H^+ and OH^-.

The method used to set up this electrochemical cell is on page 48.

2) When you electrolyse copper sulfate solution with inert electrodes:

   • <u>Copper</u> is less reactive than hydrogen, so <u>copper metal</u> is produced at the cathode (you see a coating of copper on the electrode).

$$Cu^{2+} + 2e^- \rightarrow Cu$$

   • There aren't any <u>halide ions</u> present, so <u>oxygen</u> and <u>water</u> are produced at the anode (you see bubbles of oxygen gas forming).

$$4OH^- \rightarrow O_2 + 2H_2O + 4e^-$$

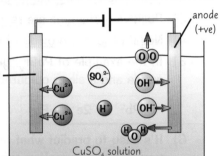

cathode (−ve)

anode (+ve)

CuSO₄ solution

Non-Inert Electrodes Take Part in Electrolysis Reactions

1) If you set up an electrochemical cell in the same way as the one above, but using <u>copper electrodes</u> in a solution of copper sulfate instead of <u>inert</u> electrodes, the result is different.

2) As the reaction continues, the <u>mass</u> of the <u>anode</u> will <u>decrease</u> and the <u>mass</u> of the <u>cathode</u> will <u>increase</u>. This is because copper is transferred from the anode to the cathode.

3) The reaction takes a bit of time to happen, you'll need to leave the cell running for <u>30 minutes</u> or so to get a decent change in mass.

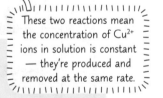

cathode (−ve)

anode (+ve)

CuSO₄ solution

4) You can measure how the mass of your electrodes has changed during an experiment like this one by finding the <u>difference</u> between the <u>masses</u> of the electrodes before and after the experiment.

5) You should make sure the electrodes are <u>dry</u> before weighing them — any copper sulfate solution on the electrodes may mean they appear to have a <u>higher mass</u> than they really do...

6) If you <u>increase the current</u> (e.g. by adding batteries) you will increase the rate of electrolysis. This means there will be a <u>bigger difference</u> between the <u>mass</u> of the two electrodes after the same amount of time.

7) The <u>electrical supply</u> acts by:

   • <u>Pulling electrons off</u> copper atoms at the <u>anode</u>: $Cu_{(s)} \rightarrow Cu^{2+}_{(aq)} + 2e^-$

   • <u>Offering electrons</u> at the <u>cathode</u> to nearby <u>Cu^{2+} ions</u>: $Cu^{2+}_{(aq)} + 2e^- \rightarrow Cu_{(s)}$

These two reactions mean the concentration of Cu^{2+} ions in solution is constant — they're produced and removed at the same rate.

<u>Copper</u> can be extracted from its ore by <u>reduction with carbon</u> (see p.55), but copper made in this way is <u>impure</u>. <u>Electrolysis</u> is used to <u>purify</u> it — this method uses an electrochemical cell with <u>copper electrodes</u>:

When copper is <u>purified</u> using <u>electrolysis</u>, the <u>anode</u> starts off as a big lump of <u>impure copper</u>, the <u>electrolyte</u> is <u>copper(II) sulfate solution</u> (which contains Cu^{2+} ions) and the <u>cathode</u> starts off as a thin piece of <u>pure copper</u>.

Here's what happens during the process:

1) The impure copper anode is <u>oxidised</u>, <u>dissolving</u> into the <u>electrolyte</u> to form <u>copper ions</u>:

$$Cu \rightarrow Cu^{2+} + 2e^-$$

2) The copper ions are <u>reduced</u> at the pure copper cathode, and add to it as a layer of <u>pure copper</u>:

$$Cu^{2+} + 2e^- \rightarrow Cu$$

3) Any <u>impurities</u> from the <u>impure copper anode</u> sink to the bottom of the cell, forming a <u>sludge</u>.

A hat, some handcuffs and a truncheon — 100% pure copper...

Phew, that's the last page on electrolysis (for now...). Time to celebrate making it to the end with a question.

Q1 Explain how electrolysis is used to purify copper for use in electrical circuits. [4 marks]

Revision Questions for Topic 3

Topic 3 had quite a few nasty pages, but you got through it. Just time for some revision questions.
- Try these questions and tick off each one when you get it right.
- When you've done all the questions under a heading and are completely happy with it, tick it off.

Acids and Bases (p.43) ☑

1) What pH value would a neutral substance have? ☑
2) What is an alkali? ☑
3) State what colours the following indicators are in acidic solutions:
   a) litmus
   b) methyl orange
   c) phenolphthalein ☑
4) Write the ionic equation for a neutralisation reaction. ☑
5) Sketch a pH curve to show how the pH changes when an excess of the base, calcium hydroxide is added to hydrochloric acid. ☑

Strong and Weak Acids (p.44) ☑

6) Write an equation to show how ethanoic acid (CH_3COOH) acts as a weak acid. ☑
7) If you increase the hydrogen ion concentration of a solution by a factor of 10, what will happen to the pH of the solution? ☑

Reactions of Acids (p.45) ☑

8) Write a chemical equation to show how hydrochloric acid reacts with copper oxide. ☑
9) Describe a test you could carry out to test for hydrogen gas. ☑
10) What would you expect to see if you bubbled carbon dioxide through limewater? ☑

Making Salts (p.46-47) ☑

11) List three insoluble sulfates. ☑
12) Name two soluble hydroxides. ☑
13) Describe how you could make a pure sample of a soluble salt from an acid and an alkali. ☑

Electrolysis (p.48-50) ☑

14) What is electrolysis? ☑
15) Towards which electrode do the anions in an electrolyte move? ☑
16) Describe how you would carry out an electrolysis where the electrolyte is a molten ionic solid. ☑
17) At which electrode does the metal form during the electrolysis of a molten ionic compound? ☑
18) Write a half equation to show what happens at the cathode in the electrolysis of copper chloride solution, $CuCl_2$. ☑
19) Why do the masses of non-inert electrodes change during electrolysis? ☑

The Reactivity Series

Reactivity series are lists of <u>metals</u> (sometimes with some <u>carbon</u> or <u>hydrogen</u> thrown in for fun). But they're not just any old lists in any old order. No siree... As the name suggests, they tell you all about <u>reactivities</u>.

If Something Gains Oxygen it's Oxidised

<u>Oxidation</u> can mean the <u>reaction with</u>, or <u>addition of oxygen</u>. <u>Reduction</u> can be the <u>removal of oxygen</u>.

E.g. $Fe_2O_3 + 3CO \rightarrow 2Fe + 3CO_2$

- <u>Iron oxide</u> is <u>reduced</u> to <u>iron</u> (as oxygen is removed).
- <u>Carbon monoxide</u> is <u>oxidised</u> to <u>carbon dioxide</u> (as oxygen is added).

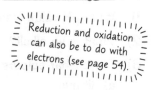
Reduction and oxidation can also be to do with electrons (see page 54).

<u>Combustion</u> reactions involve <u>oxidation</u>. They're always <u>exothermic</u> (see page 83).

E.g. $CH_4 + 2O_2 \rightarrow CO_2 + 2H_2O$

- Both the <u>carbon</u> and <u>hydrogen</u> are <u>oxidised</u> — they gain oxygen.
- The <u>oxygen molecules</u> are <u>reduced</u> as the oxygen atoms get split up by the reaction.

The Reactivity Series Shows How Easily Metals Are Oxidised

1) A <u>reactivity series</u> is a table that lists <u>metals</u> in order of their <u>reactivity</u>.

2) As well as the metals, <u>carbon</u> is often included in reactivity series — a metal's position in the reactivity series compared to carbon dictates how it's <u>extracted from its ore</u> (see pages 55-56).

3) <u>Hydrogen</u> can be included in the reactivity series too — this shows the reactivity of metals with <u>dilute acids</u> (see next page).

4) Here's an <u>example</u> of a reactivity series:

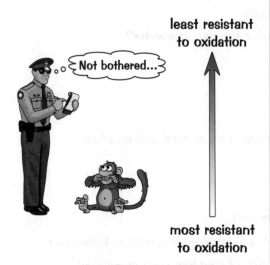
Not bothered...

least resistant to oxidation ↑   most resistant to oxidation ↑

The Reactivity Series		
Potassium	K	most reactive
Sodium	Na	
Calcium	Ca	
Magnesium	Mg	
Aluminium	Al	
Carbon	C	
Zinc	Zn	
Iron	Fe	
Hydrogen	H	
Copper	Cu	
Silver	Ag	least reactive
Gold	Au	

If a metal is below hydrogen in the reactivity series, it's less reactive than hydrogen and won't react with dilute acids.

Because metals at the top of the reactivity series are less resistant to oxidation, they corrode easily. Metals at the bottom are more resistant to corrosion (see page 64 for more on corrosion).

5) The metals at the <u>top</u> of the reactivity series are the <u>most reactive</u> — they easily lose their electrons to form <u>cations</u> (<u>positive ions</u>). They're also <u>oxidised easily</u>.

6) The metals at the bottom of the reactivity series are <u>less reactive</u> — they don't give up their electrons to form cations as easily. They're more <u>resistant to oxidation</u> than the metals higher up the reactivity series.

7) You can determine a metal's position in the reactivity series by reacting it with <u>water</u> and <u>dilute acids</u> (see next page).

I told a hilarious joke to some sodium — the reaction was great...

You could come across different reactivity series to the one shown above. But panic not noble chemistry pal... they all work the same. The more reactive elements are at the top of the series and the less reactive ones are at the bottom.

Q1   Identify which element has been oxidised in the following reaction: $CuO + H_2 \rightarrow Cu + H_2O$ [1 mark]

Q2   Using the reactivity series above, explain whether copper or calcium is more easily oxidised.   [1 mark]

Reactivity of Metals

Reactive metals tend to do exciting, fizzy things when you drop them into acid or water...

How Metals React With Acids Tells You About Their Reactivity

1) The more easily a metal atom loses its outer electrons and forms a positive ion, the more reactive it will be.

2) Here's a classic experiment that you can do to show that some metals are more reactive than others. All you do is to place little pieces of various metals into dilute hydrochloric acid:

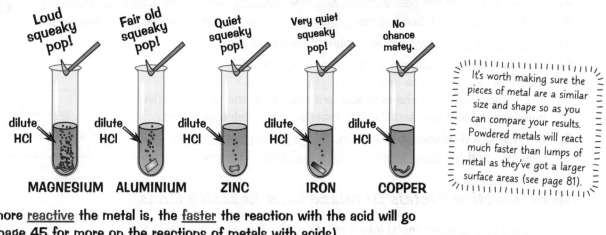

It's worth making sure the pieces of metal are a similar size and shape so as you can compare your results. Powdered metals will react much faster than lumps of metal as they've got a larger surface areas (see page 81).

3) The more reactive the metal is, the faster the reaction with the acid will go (see page 45 for more on the reactions of metals with acids).

4) Very reactive metals (e.g. magnesium) will fizz vigorously, less reactive metals (e.g. zinc) will bubble a bit, and unreactive metals (e.g. copper) will not react with dilute acids at all.

5) You can show that hydrogen is forming using the burning splint test (see page 45). The louder the squeaky pop, the more hydrogen has been made in the time period and the more reactive the metal is.

6) The speed of reaction is also indicated by the rate at which the bubbles of hydrogen are given off — the faster the bubbles form, the faster the reaction and the more reactive the metal.

You could also follow the rate of the reaction by using a gas syringe to measure the volume of gas given off at regular time intervals (see p.77) or using a thermometer to measure by how much the temperature changes (as the reaction of acids with metals is exothermic — see p.83).

Some Metals Also React With Water

The reactions of metals with water also show the reactivity of metals. This is the basic reaction:

> metal + water → metal hydroxide + hydrogen
> (Or: less reactive metal + steam → metal oxide + hydrogen)

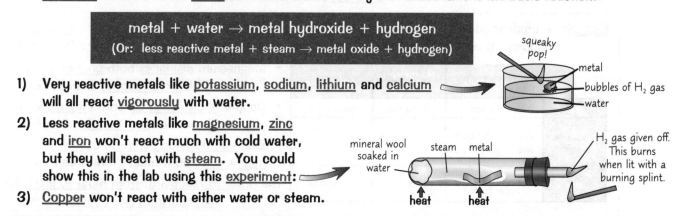

1) Very reactive metals like potassium, sodium, lithium and calcium will all react vigorously with water.

2) Less reactive metals like magnesium, zinc and iron won't react much with cold water, but they will react with steam. You could show this in the lab using this experiment:

3) Copper won't react with either water or steam.

I AM NOT HIGHLY REACTIVE — OK...

This stuff isn't too bad — who knows, you might even get to have a go at these experiments in class...

Q1 A student is given small samples of three metals, A, B and C. He places them in dilute hydrochloric acid. Nothing happens to Metal A. Metal B fizzes vigorously. The gas given off gives a loud squeaky pop when lit with a burning splint. Metal C fizzes a bit. The gas given off gives a quiet squeaky pop when lit.
   a) Put the three metals in order, from most reactive to least reactive. [1 mark]
   b) One of the metals was zinc, one was magnesium, and one was copper. Use this information to identify metals A, B and C. [1 mark]

Displacement Reactions

As well as by reacting metals with <u>dilute acids</u> and <u>water</u>, you can directly compare the reactivity of metals using <u>displacement reactions</u>. This involves reacting metals with <u>metal salt solutions</u>. Exciting stuff I tell ya.

Displacement Reactions are Redox Reactions

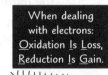

1) As well as talking about <u>reduction</u> and <u>oxidation</u> in terms of the loss and gain of <u>oxygen</u> (as on page 52), you can also talk about them in terms of <u>electrons</u> (as in electrolysis).

2) <u>Oxidation</u> can be the <u>loss of electrons</u>, and <u>reduction</u> can be the <u>gain of electrons</u>.

3) Reduction and oxidation happen <u>simultaneously</u> — hence the name <u>redox</u> reactions.

4) <u>Displacement reactions</u> are examples of redox reactions.

5) In displacement reactions, a <u>more reactive element</u> reacts to take the place of a <u>less reactive element</u> in a compound. In metal displacement reactions, the more reactive metal loses electrons and the less reactive metal gains electrons.

When dealing with electrons: Oxidation <u>I</u>s <u>L</u>oss, Reduction <u>I</u>s <u>G</u>ain.

Remember it as OIL RIG.

6) So, during a displacement reaction, the <u>more reactive metal</u> is <u>oxidised</u>, and the <u>less reactive metal</u> is <u>reduced</u>. For example:

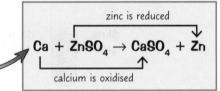

zinc is reduced

$$Ca + ZnSO_4 \rightarrow CaSO_4 + Zn$$

calcium is oxidised

More Reactive Metals Displace Less Reactive Ones

1) If you put a <u>reactive metal</u> into a solution of a <u>less reactive metal salt</u>, the reactive metal will <u>replace</u> the <u>less reactive metal</u> in the salt.

> <u>Example</u>: if you put an <u>iron nail</u> in a solution of <u>copper sulfate</u>, the more reactive iron will "<u>kick out</u>" the less reactive copper from the salt. You end up with <u>iron sulfate solution</u> and <u>copper metal</u>.
>
> copper sulfate + iron → iron sulfate + copper
> $$CuSO_4 + Fe \rightarrow FeSO_4 + Cu$$
>
> In this reaction, copper is reduced and iron is oxidised.

2) If you put a <u>less reactive metal</u> into a solution of a <u>more reactive metal salt</u>, <u>nothing</u> will happen.

> <u>Example</u>: if you put a small piece of silver metal into a solution of <u>copper sulfate</u>, nothing will happen. The more reactive metal (copper) is already in the salt.

3) You can use displacement reactions to <u>work out</u> where in the reactivity series a metal should go.

> <u>Example</u>: A student adds some <u>metals</u> to <u>metal salt solutions</u> and records whether any <u>reactions</u> happen. Use her table of results, below, to work out an <u>order of reactivity</u> for the metals.

	copper nitrate	magnesium chloride	zinc sulfate
copper	no reaction	no reaction	no reaction
magnesium	magnesium nitrate and copper formed	no reaction	magnesium sulfate and zinc formed
zinc	zinc nitrate and copper formed	no reaction	no reaction

- Magnesium <u>displaces</u> both <u>copper</u> and <u>zinc</u>, so it must be <u>more reactive</u> than both.
- Copper <u>is displaced by</u> both <u>magnesium</u> and <u>zinc</u>, so it must be <u>less reactive</u> than both.
- Zinc <u>can displace copper</u>, but <u>not magnesium</u>, so it must go between them.

The <u>order of reactivity</u>, <u>from most to least</u>, is: <u>magnesium, zinc, copper</u>.

And that's why Iron Man never goes swimming in copper sulfate...

You could be given the results of an experiment and have to use them to put the metals into an order of reactivity, or you could be told their reactivities and then asked to predict how they'll react — make sure you can do both. Time for some questions anyway — you may want to use the reactivity series on page 52 to help you...

Q1   State whether silver would displace iron from iron chloride solution and explain your answer.   [1 mark]

Q2   Lithium sits between sodium and calcium in the reactivity series.
State whether lithium would displace zinc from zinc sulfate solution and explain your answer.   [1 mark]

Extracting Metals Using Carbon

A few <u>unreactive metals</u>, like gold, are found in the Earth as the metals themselves, rather than as a compound. The rest of the metals we get by <u>extracting</u> them <u>from rocks</u> — and I bet you're just itching to find out how...

Ores Contain Enough Metal to Make Extraction Worthwhile

1) A <u>metal ore</u> is a <u>rock</u> which contains <u>enough metal</u> to make it <u>economically worthwhile</u> extracting the metal from it. In many cases the ore is an <u>oxide</u> of the metal.

> <u>Example</u>: the main <u>aluminium ore</u> is called <u>bauxite</u> — it's aluminium oxide (Al_2O_3).

Row faster men!

We can't — it's these cursed metal oars.

2) Most of the metals that we use are found in their <u>ores</u> in the <u>Earth's crust</u>. The ores are mined and the metals can then be <u>extracted</u> from the ores.

3) Some <u>unreactive metals</u>, such as gold and platinum, are present in the Earth's crust as <u>uncombined elements</u>. These metals can be mined straight out of the ground, but they usually need to be <u>refined</u> before they can be used.

Some Metals can be Extracted by Reduction with Carbon

1) A metal can be <u>extracted</u> from its ore chemically by <u>reduction</u> using <u>carbon</u>.

2) When an ore is reduced, <u>oxygen is removed</u> from it, e.g.

> $$2Fe_2O_3 \quad + \quad 3C \quad \rightarrow \quad 4Fe \quad + \quad 3CO_2$$
> iron oxide + carbon → iron + carbon dioxide

Most of the time, you actually get a mixture of carbon dioxide CO_2 and carbon monoxide (CO) when you reduce metal oxides with carbon.

3) The position of the metal in the <u>reactivity series</u> determines whether it can be extracted by <u>reduction</u> with carbon.

See page 52 for more on reactivity series.

- Metals <u>higher than carbon</u> in the reactivity series have to be extracted using <u>electrolysis</u> (see next page) which is expensive.

- Metals <u>below carbon</u> in the reactivity series can be extracted by <u>reduction</u> using <u>carbon</u>. For example, <u>iron oxide</u> is reduced in a <u>blast furnace</u> to make <u>iron</u>.

- This is because carbon <u>can only take</u> the <u>oxygen</u> away from metals which are <u>less reactive</u> than carbon <u>itself</u> is.

Extracted using <u>electrolysis</u>

Extracted by <u>reduction</u> using <u>carbon</u>

Found as <u>uncombined elements</u>

The Reactivity Series

Potassium	K	more reactive
Sodium	Na	
Calcium	Ca	
Magnesium	Mg	
Aluminium	Al	
<u>CARBON</u>	<u>C</u>	
Zinc	Zn	
Iron	Fe	
Tin	Sn	
Copper	Cu	
Silver	Ag	
Gold	Au	less reactive

[Please insert ore-ful pun here]...

Make sure you've got that reactivity series sorted in your head. If a metal's below carbon in the reactivity series, then it's less reactive than carbon and can be extracted from its ore by reduction using carbon. Phew... got it?

Q1 How would you extract tin from its metal ore? Explain your answer. [2 marks]

Q2 Write a balanced chemical equation to describe the reaction that occurs when carbon is used to extract zinc from its ore, zinc oxide (ZnO). [2 marks]

Other Methods of Extracting Metals

Electrolysis is an expensive process but, like many pricey things, it's really rather good...

Some Metals have to be Extracted by Electrolysis

1) Metals that are more reactive than carbon (see previous page) are extracted using electrolysis of molten compounds (see page 48 for more on this).

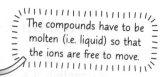
The compounds have to be molten (i.e. liquid) so that the ions are free to move.

2) Once the metal ore is melted, an electric current is passed through it. The metal is discharged at the cathode and the non-metal at the anode.

Example: Aluminium is extracted from its ore using electrolysis with carbon electrodes. Aluminium oxide (Al_2O_3) has a high melting point, so the ore is first dissolved in molten cryolite (an aluminium compound with a lower melting point than Al_2O_3) to lower the melting point. The ions in this molten mixture are free to move.
During the electrolysis, aluminium is formed at the cathode: $Al^{3+} + 3e^- \rightarrow Al$
Oxygen forms at the anode: $2O^{2-} \rightarrow O_2 + 4e^-$
The overall equation is: $2Al_2O_{3(l)} \rightarrow 4Al_{(l)} + 3O_{2(g)}$

Aluminium metal sinks to the bottom of the cell and is siphoned off.

Electrolysis is a More Expensive Process than Reduction with Carbon

1) In order to run electrolysis to extract metals from their ores, you need large amounts of electricity. Electricity is expensive, making electrolysis a pretty pricey process. There are also costs associated with melting or dissolving the metal ore so it can conduct electricity.

2) In comparison, extracting metals using reduction with carbon is much cheaper. Carbon is cheap, and also acts as a fuel to provide the heat needed for the reduction reaction to happen.

3) This means that, in general, metals lower down the reactivity series (less reactive metals) are cheaper to extract than those higher up the reactivity series (more reactive metals).

There are Biological Methods to Extract Metals

We can also recycle metals to save resources (see next page).

1) The supply of some metal rich ores, e.g. copper ore, is limited.

2) The demand for lots of metals is growing and this may lead to shortages in the future.

3) Scientists are looking into new ways of extracting metals from low-grade ores (ores that only contain small amounts of the metal) or from the waste that is currently produced when metals are extracted.

4) Examples of new methods to extract metals from their ores are bioleaching and phytoextraction. These are biological methods as they use living organisms.

Bioleaching: This uses bacteria to separate metals from their ores, e.g. copper can be separated from copper sulfide this way. The bacteria get energy from the bonds between the atoms in the ore, separating out the metal from the ore in the process. The leachate (the solution produced by the process) contains metal ions, which can be extracted, e.g. by electrolysis or displacement (see page 54) with a more reactive metal.

This is a bacterial method of extracting metals.

Phytoextraction: This involves growing plants in soil that contains metal compounds. The plants can't use or get rid of the metals so they gradually build up in the leaves. The plants can be harvested, dried and burned in a furnace. The ash contains metal compounds from which the metal can be extracted by electrolysis or displacement reactions.

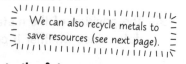

5) Traditional methods of mining are pretty damaging to the environment (see the next page). These new methods of extraction have a much smaller impact, but the disadvantage is that they're slow.

A policeman failed his maths test — he's a low-grade copper...

Make sure you can remember all those techniques for extracting metals, even those snazzy biological methods.

Q1   Use the reactivity series on page 55 to predict whether aluminium or iron would be more expensive to extract from its ore. Explain your answer.   [3 marks]

Recycling

Recycling's a hot topic. We don't have an infinite amount of materials, e.g. metals, to keep on making things from, so recycling's really important to make sure we don't run out of lots of important raw materials.

Recycling Conserves Resources and Energy

1) Extracting raw materials can take large amounts of energy, lots of which comes from burning fossil fuels.

2) Fossil fuels are running out (they're a non-renewable resource) so it's important to conserve them. Not only this, but burning them contributes to acid rain and climate change (see pages 89 and 93).

3) Recycling materials saves energy as this process often only uses a small fraction of the energy needed to extract and refine the material from scratch.

4) As there's a finite amount of many raw materials, e.g. metals, on Earth, recycling conserves these resources too. Metals, like fossil fuels, are non-renewable.

5) It's particularly important to recycle materials that are rare.

Recycling Protects the Environment

1) Extracting metals also impacts on the environment. Mines are damaging to the environment and destroy habitats — not to mention the fact that they're a bit of an eyesore. Recycling more metals means that we don't need so many mines.

2) Recycling materials also cuts down on the amount of rubbish that gets sent to landfill. Landfill takes up space and pollutes the surroundings.

Recycling Has Important Economic Benefits

1) As you saw above, extracting materials often requires more energy than just recycling them, and energy doesn't come cheap. So recycling saves money.

2) It is particularly beneficial to the economy to recycle metals that are expensive to extract or buy.

3) Recycling is also a massive industry and creates lots of jobs. The materials to be recycled need to be transported to and processed at recycling centres. They then need to be reprocessed into new products which can be sold.

4) Jobs are created at every stage of this process — far more than are created by simply disposing of waste by dumping it into landfill.

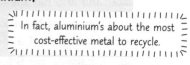

Example: Recycling Aluminium

1) If you didn't recycle aluminium, you'd have to mine more aluminium ore — 4 tonnes for every 1 tonne of aluminium you need. But mining makes a mess of the landscape (and these mines are often in rainforests). The ore then needs to be transported, and the aluminium extracted (which uses loads of electricity). And don't forget the cost of sending your used aluminium to landfill.

2) So it's a complex calculation, but for every 1 kg of aluminium cans you recycle, you save:
   - 95% or so of the energy needed to mine and extract 'fresh' aluminium,
   - 4 kg of aluminium ore,
   - a lot of waste.

In fact, aluminium's about the most cost-effective metal to recycle.

I told a hilarious joke to some sodium — the reaction was great...

Cracking jokes like the ones you find in this book grow on trees you know. So to save trees and reduce the environmental costs of this book, I thought I'd recycle that hilarious pun from page 52. Aren't I good?

Q1   Material X is a metal. To recycle material X you need 110% of the energy used to extract and refine it. Explain why it might still be better to recycle material X.   [2 marks]

Life Cycle Assessments

If a company wants to manufacture a new product, it will carry out a <u>life cycle assessment</u> (LCA). Fun stuff.

Life Cycle Assessments Show Total Environmental Costs

A <u>life cycle assessment (LCA)</u> looks at each <u>stage</u> of the <u>life</u> of a product —
from making the <u>material</u> from natural raw materials, to making the <u>product</u> from
the material, <u>using</u> the product and <u>disposing</u> of the product.
It works out the potential <u>environmental impact</u> of each stage.

Choice of material

1) <u>Metals</u> have to be <u>mined</u> and <u>extracted</u> from their ores.
   These processes need a lot of <u>energy</u> and cause a lot of <u>pollution</u>.

2) <u>Raw materials</u> for chemical manufacture often come from <u>crude oil</u>. Crude oil is a
   <u>non-renewable resource</u>, and supplies are <u>decreasing</u>. Also, obtaining crude oil from the
   ground and refining it into useful raw materials requires a lot of <u>energy</u> and generates <u>pollution</u>.

Manufacture

1) <u>Manufacturing</u> products uses a lot of <u>energy</u> and other resources.

2) It can also cause a lot of <u>pollution</u>, e.g. <u>harmful fumes</u> such as CO or HCl.

3) You also need to think about any <u>waste</u> products and how to <u>dispose</u> of them.

4) Some waste can be <u>recycled</u> and turned into other <u>useful chemicals</u>,
   reducing the amount that ends up polluting the environment.

5) Most chemical manufacture needs <u>water</u>. Businesses have to make sure they
   don't put <u>polluted</u> water back into the environment at the end of the process.

Product Use

<u>Using</u> the product can also damage the environment. For example:

1) <u>Paint</u> gives off <u>toxic fumes</u>.

2) <u>Burning fuels</u> releases <u>greenhouse gases</u> and other <u>harmful substances</u>.

3) <u>Fertilisers</u> can <u>leach</u> into streams and rivers and cause damage to <u>ecosystems</u>.

Disposal

1) Products are often <u>disposed</u> of in a <u>landfill</u> site at the end of their life.

2) This takes up space and can <u>pollute</u> land and water.

3) Products might be <u>incinerated</u> (burnt), which causes air pollution.

Some products can be disposed of by being recycled (see page 57).

EXAMPLE: A company is carrying out a
life cycle assessment to work out which car,
A, B or C, it should make. Using the data in
the table, explain which car the company should
produce to minimise the environmental impact.

Car	CO₂ emissions (tonnes)	Waste solid produced (kg)	Water used (m³)	Expected lifespan of product (years)
A	17	10 720	8.2	11
B	21	5900	6.0	17
C	34	15 010	9.5	12

- Car A produces the least CO_2, but produces the second highest amount of waste solids
  and uses the second highest amount of water. It also has the shortest life span.

- Car B produces more CO_2 than car A, but produces by far the least waste solid, uses the least
  water and also has the longest life span. On balance, this looks a better choice than car A.

- Car C produces the most CO_2, the most waste solid, uses the most water, and
  has almost as short a life span as car A. This looks like the worst choice.

  So, on balance, **car B** looks like the one that will have the least environmental impact.

My cycle assessment — two wheels, a bell, an uncomfortable seat...

Don't get your bike cycle and life cycle assessments confused. Life cycle assessments are the ones you'll need.

Q1   For the example above, suggest four further things (that aren't outlined in the table)
      that the company should consider when forming a life cycle assessment for the car.   [4 marks]

Dynamic Equilibrium

Reversible reactions — products forming from reactants and reactants forming from products. I can't keep up...

Reversible Reactions can go Forwards and Backwards

A reversible reaction is one where the products can react with each other to produce the original reactants. In other words, it can go both ways.

$$A + B \rightleftharpoons C + D$$

The '$\rightleftharpoons$' shows that the reaction goes both ways.

The Haber process (see page 68) is an example of a reversible reaction.

1) During the Haber process, nitrogen and hydrogen react to form ammonia: $N_2 + 3H_2 \rightleftharpoons 2NH_3$
   - The nitrogen (N_2) is obtained easily from the air, which is about 78% nitrogen.
   - The hydrogen (H_2) can be extracted from hydrocarbons from sources such as natural gas and crude oil.

2) The Haber process is carried out at 450 °C, with a pressure of 200 atmospheres and an iron catalyst.

Reversible Reactions Will Reach Equilibrium

1) As the reactants (A and B) react, their concentrations fall — so the forward reaction will slow down. But as more and more of the products (C and D) are made and their concentrations rise, the backward reaction will speed up.

See the next page for more on concentrations and rate.

2) After a while the forward reaction will be going at exactly the same rate as the backward one — this is equilibrium.

3) At equilibrium both reactions are still happening, but there's no overall effect.

4) This is a dynamic equilibrium — the forward and backward reactions are both happening at the same time and at the same rate, and the concentrations of reactants and products have reached a balance and won't change.

5) Equilibrium can only be reached if the reversible reaction takes place in a 'closed system'. A closed system just means that none of the reactants or products can escape.

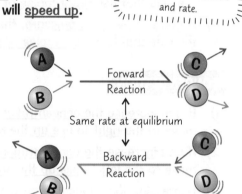

Forward Reaction

Same rate at equilibrium

Backward Reaction

When a reaction's at equilibrium it doesn't mean that the amounts of reactants and products are equal.
- Sometimes the equilibrium will lie to the right — this basically means "lots of the products and not much of the reactants" (i.e. the concentration of products is greater than the concentration of reactants).
- Sometimes the equilibrium will lie to the left — this basically means "lots of the reactants but not much of the products" (the concentration of reactants is greater than the concentration of products).
- The exact position of equilibrium depends on the conditions (as well as the reaction itself).

Three Things Can Change the Position of Equilibrium

Three things can change the position of equilibrium (which changes the amounts of products and reactants present at equilibrium). These are temperature, pressure (for equilibria involving gases) and concentrations (of reactants or products).

The plural of equilibrium is 'equilibria'.

Example: ammonium chloride $\rightleftharpoons$ ammonia + hydrogen chloride
Heating this reaction moves the equilibrium to the right (more ammonia and hydrogen chloride) and cooling it moves it to the left (more ammonium chloride).

Dynamic equilibrium — lots of activity, but not to any great effect...*

Keep an eagle eye out for that arrow that shows you that a reaction is reversible. I'd hate you to miss it.

Q1   Explain what is meant by the term 'reversible reaction'.   [1 mark]

Q2   What is dynamic equilibrium?   [3 marks]

*a bit like the England football team.

Le Chatelier's Principle

This stuff might feel a bit complicated to start with, but it all comes down to one simple rule — whatever you do to a reversible reaction, the equilibrium position will move to try to undo your change. How contrary...

The Equilibrium Position Moves to Minimise Any Changes You Make

Le Chatelier's principle states that if there's a change in concentration, pressure or temperature in a reversible reaction, the equilibrium position will move to help counteract that change.

TEMPERATURE All reactions are exothermic in one direction and endothermic in the other (see page 83).

1) If you decrease the temperature, the equilibrium will move in the exothermic direction to produce more heat.

2) If you increase the temperature, the equilibrium will move in the endothermic direction to absorb the extra heat.

> For example: $N_2 + 3H_2 \rightleftharpoons 2NH_3$
> This reaction is exothermic in the forward direction.
> If you decrease the temperature, the equilibrium will shift to the right (so you'll make more product).

PRESSURE Changing this only affects equilibria involving gases.

1) If you increase the pressure, the equilibrium will move towards the side that has fewer moles of gas to reduce pressure.

2) If you decrease the pressure, the equilibrium will move towards the side that has more moles of gas to increase pressure.

> For example:
> $N_2 + 3H_2 \rightleftharpoons 2NH_3$
> This reaction has 4 moles of gas on the left and 2 on the right. If you increase the pressure, the equilibrium will shift to the right (so you'll make more product).

CONCENTRATION

1) If you increase the concentration of the reactants, the equilibrium will move to the right to use up the reactants (making more products).

2) If you increase the concentration of the products, the equilibrium will move to the left to use up the products (making more reactants).

3) Decreasing the concentration will have the opposite effect.

> For example:
> $N_2 + 3H_2 \rightleftharpoons 2NH_3$
> If you increase the concentration of N_2 or H_2, the equilibrium will shift to the right to use up the extra reactants (so you'll make more product).

You Can Predict How the Position of Equilibrium Will Change

You can apply the rules above to any reversible reaction to work out how changing the conditions will affect the equilibrium position. This has useful applications in industry — you can increase yield (see page 66) by changing the conditions to shift the equilibrium position to the right (towards the products).

EXAMPLE:

The compound PCl_5 can be made using this reaction: $PCl_{3\,(g)} + Cl_{2\,(g)} \rightleftharpoons PCl_{5\,(g)}$

Explain what would happen to the equilibrium position and to the yield of PCl_5 if you increased the pressure that the reaction was being performed at.

According to Le Chatelier's Principle, if you increase the pressure, the position of equilibrium will move towards the side with fewer moles of gas to reduce the pressure. In this reaction there are 2 moles of gas in the reactants and 1 in the products.

The position of equilibrium will move to the right, since that is the side with fewer moles of gas. This shifts the equilibrium towards the products, so the yield of PCl_5 will increase.

Le Chatelier — relieving pressure since 1884...

Le Chatelier's principle may relieve the pressure in chemical systems, but it stands a chance of giving you a right headache in the exam. So, best make sure you understand it now by trying these questions...

Q1 This reaction is endothermic in the forward direction: $CH_3OH_{(g)} \rightleftharpoons CO_{(g)} + 2H_{2\,(g)}$. What will happen to the position of equilibrium if the temperature is increased? Explain your answer. [2 marks]

Q2 What would happen to the yield of SO_3 in the reaction below if the pressure was decreased? Explain your answer. $2SO_{2\,(g)} + O_{2\,(g)} \rightleftharpoons 2SO_{3\,(g)}$ [3 marks]

Revision Questions for Topic 4

Topic 4 was a gem wasn't it? Those reactivity series could prove tricky though, so try these questions.

- Try these questions and <u>tick off each one</u> when you <u>get it right</u>.
- When you've done <u>all the questions</u> under a heading and are <u>completely happy</u> with it, tick it off.

The Reactions and Reactivity of Metals (p.52-54) ☑

1) Describe oxidation and reduction in terms of the addition and removal of oxygen. ☑
2) Identify which element is reduced in the following reaction: $CH_4 + 2O_2 \rightarrow CO_2 + 2H_2O$ ☑
3) In a reactivity series, where do you find the least reactive elements? ☑
4) True or false? The easier it is for a metal atom to form a positive ion, the more reactive it will be. ☑
5) You are given samples of four mystery metals and some dilute hydrochloric acid.
   Briefly describe how you could use these things to work out a reactivity series for the four metals. ☑
6) Describe oxidation and reduction in terms of electrons. ☑
7) What is a redox reaction? ☑
8) Describe what happens during a displacement reaction. ☑

Extracting Metals from their Ores (p.55-56) ☑

9) What is a metal ore and where are they usually found? ☑
10) How are metals more reactive than carbon usually extracted from their ores? ☑
11) Describe how metals less reactive than carbon are usually extracted from their ores. ☑
12) Name two biological methods that can be used to extract metals from low-grade ores. ☑
13) Give an advantage and a disadvantage of using bioleaching, rather than electrolysis, to extract metals. ☑

Conserving Resources (p.57-58) ☑

14) Give two ways in which recycling is better for the environment than disposing of waste in landfill. ☑
15) State how recycling can benefit the economy. ☑
16) What is a life cycle assessment? ☑
17) Name four factors that should be considered when drawing up a life cycle assessment for a product. ☑

Equilibria (p.59-60) ☑

18) Draw the symbol which shows that a reaction is reversible. ☑
19) If the position of equilibrium for a reversible reaction lies to the right,
   what does that tell you about the relative amounts of reactants and products present? ☑
20) State Le Chatelier's principle. ☑
21) Describe what would happen to the equilibrium position of a reversible reaction
   if you increased the concentration of the reactants. ☑

Transition Metals

You'll find the transition metals sitting together slap bang in the middle of the periodic table. They've got plenty of different properties that you need to know about — so grab a cup of tea and a biscuit, and read on...

The Transition Metals Sit in the Middle of the Periodic Table

A lot of everyday metals are transition metals (e.g. copper, iron, zinc, gold, silver, platinum) — but there are loads of others as well.

If you get asked about a transition metal you've never heard of — don't panic. These 'new' transition metals will follow all the properties you've already learnt for the others.

These are the transition metals

Sc	Ti	V	Cr	Mn	Fe	Co	Ni	Cu	Zn
Y	Zr	Nb	Mo	Tc	Ru	Rh	Pd	Ag	Cd
La	Hf	Ta	W	Re	Os	Ir	Pt	Au	Hg
Ac	Rf	Db	Sg	Bh	Hs	Mt	Ds	Rg	Cn

Transition metals can be called transition elements.

Transition Metals Have Typical Metallic Properties

1) The transition metals have all the typical properties of metals (see page 25) — they're relatively hard, strong, shiny and malleable materials that conduct heat and electricity well.

2) They have high melting points (with the exception of mercury, which is liquid at room temperature).

3) They also have high densities. For example, at room temperature, potassium (a Group 1 metal) has a density of 0.9 g cm^{-3}, while copper has a density of 9.0 g cm^{-3}, and iron has a density of 7.9 g cm^{-3}.

4) The properties of some transition metals make them really useful. For example, gold is used in jewellery because it's shiny and malleable, but it's also a great electrical conductor and really corrosion resistant, so it's used in some electronic components. Copper is used for water pipes because it's malleable and corrosion resistant. It's another good electrical conductor, so it's used in a lot of electrical wiring.

Transition Metals and Their Compounds Make Good Catalysts

1) A catalyst speeds up the rate of a reaction without being changed or used up itself — see page 82 for more about catalysts.

2) Iron is the catalyst used in the Haber process for making ammonia (see p.68).

3) Vanadium pentoxide (V_2O_5) is the catalyst for making sulfuric acid in the Contact process.

Did you send for me?

No, I said iron catalyst.

Transition Metal Compounds are Very Colourful

The compounds of transition metals are colourful. What colour they are depends on what transition metal ion they contain — e.g. compounds containing Fe^{2+} ions are usually light green, ones with Fe^{3+} ions are orange/brown (e.g. rust, see page 64) and those with Cu^{2+} ions are often blue.

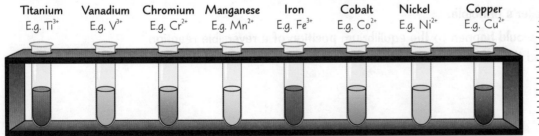

| Titanium E.g. Ti^{3+} | Vanadium E.g. V^{3+} | Chromium E.g. Cr^{2+} | Manganese E.g. Mn^{2+} | Iron E.g. Fe^{3+} | Cobalt E.g. Co^{2+} | Nickel E.g. Ni^{2+} | Copper E.g. Cu^{2+} |

You don't need to learn all these colours — they're just examples. Just be aware that transition metals can form colourful compounds.

You can't get much more colourful than transition metal ions...

Transition metals are everywhere. They make good catalysts, iron's used to make steel for construction, copper's used in electrical wiring, and you can even use their pretty compounds to colour stained glass.

Q1   Name one industrial process that uses a transition metal catalyst. Name the catalyst used.   [1 mark]

Q2   Rubidium is a Group 1 metal. Palladium is a transition metal.
Predict which of these two metals will have a higher density. Explain your answer.   [1 mark]

Alloys

Pure metals often aren't quite right for certain jobs. But instead of just making do with what they've got, scientists mix stuff in with the metals to make them behave exactly how they need them to.

Alloys are Harder Than Pure Metals

1) Pure metals are malleable (easily shaped by hammering) because they have a regular arrangement of identical atoms. The layers of ions can slide over each other.

2) This means some metals aren't strong enough for certain uses, so alloys are used instead. Alloys are made by adding another element to a metal — that could be a non-metal or another metal.

3) Different elements have different sized atoms. So, for example, when an element such as carbon is added to pure iron, the smaller carbon atoms will upset the layers of pure iron atoms, making it more difficult for them to slide over each other. So alloys are stronger.

4) Many metals in use today are actually alloys. Because we understand about the properties of metals, alloys can be designed for specific uses.

For more on the structure of metals have a look at p.25.

Pure Metals Don't Always Have the Properties Needed

1) For example, alloys of iron called steels are often used instead of pure iron. Steels are made by adding small amounts of carbon to the pure iron. Other metals are added as well to make alloy steels.

2) Steel is harder than iron. It's also stronger than iron, as long as the amount of carbon does not get greater than about 1%.

3) Iron on its own will rust (corrode) fairly quickly, but steel is much less likely to rust. A small amount of carbon makes a big difference.

4) A lot of things are made from steel — girders, bridges, engine parts, cutlery, washing machines, pans, ships, tools, cars etc.

5) Many other alloys are used everyday life:

TYPE OF STEEL	PROPERTIES
Low carbon steel (0.1–0.3% carbon)	easily shaped
High carbon steel (0.22–2.5% carbon)	very strong, inflexible, brittle
Stainless steel (chromium added, and sometimes nickel)	corrosion-resistant, strong

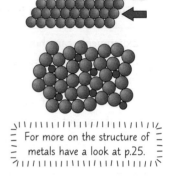

- Bronze = Copper + Tin: Bronze is harder than copper. It's used to make medals, decorative ornaments and statues.

- Brass = Copper + Zinc: Brass is more malleable than bronze and is used in situations where lower friction is required, such as in water taps and door fittings.

- Gold alloys are used to make jewellery: Pure gold is very soft and malleable. Metals such as zinc, copper, and silver are used to strengthen the gold. Pure gold is described as 24 carat, so 18 carats means that 18 out of 24 parts of the alloy are pure gold. In other words, 18 carat gold is 75% gold. For example, an 18 carat gold ring with a mass of 20 g contains 20 × (18 ÷ 24) = 15 g of gold.

- Aluminium alloys are used to make aircraft: Aluminium has a low density which is an important property in aircraft manufacture. But pure aluminium is not strong enough for making aeroplanes, so it's alloyed with small amounts of other metals to increase its strength.

- Magnalium = Aluminium + Magnesium: When it's made with small amounts of magnesium (about 5%), magnalium is stronger, lighter and corrodes less easily than pure aluminium. This type of magnalium is used to make parts for cars and aeroplanes. Magnalium with a higher magnesium content (about 50%) is used in fireworks, as it's reactive and burns brightly, like magnesium, but is more stable than pure magnesium.

If Iron Man and the Silver Surfer teamed up, they'd be great alloys...

Life would be pretty different without alloys around. I'd have to cancel my trumpet recital for a start...

Q1 Give one use of steel. [1 mark]

Q2 Explain why alloys of aluminium are used instead of pure aluminium for building aircraft. [1 mark]

Corrosion

Corrosion (e.g. rusting) is a process where something is slowly damaged or destroyed by a chemical process.

Rusting of Iron is a Redox Reaction

1) Metals can corrode in the presence of oxygen and water to form their metal oxides.

2) Corrosion of metals is caused by redox reactions. The metal loses electrons, so it's oxidised. Simultaneously, oxygen gains electrons when it reacts with the metal.

3) Rusting is the name for the corrosion of iron. Rusting only happens when the iron is in contact with both oxygen (from the air) and water.

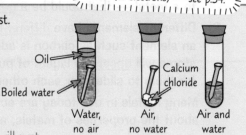
Remember OIL RIG — Oxidation is Loss, Reduction is Gain (of electrons) — see p.54.

Experiments can show that both oxygen and water are needed for iron to rust.

- If you put an iron nail in a boiling tube with just water, it won't rust. Boiling the water beforehand will remove oxygen, and oil can be used to stop air getting in.

- If you put an iron nail in a boiling tube with just air, it won't rust. Calcium chloride can be used to absorb any water from the air.

- However, if you put an iron nail in a boiling tube with air and water, it will rust.

Oil
Calcium chloride
Boiled water
Water, no air
Air, no water
Air and water

There are Different Ways to Prevent Rusting

1) You can prevent rusting by coating the iron with a barrier. This keeps out the water, oxygen or both.

2) Painting is ideal for large and small structures. It can also be nice and colourful.

3) Oiling or greasing has to be used when moving parts are involved, like on bike chains.

4) You can also prevent rusting using sacrificial protection — this involves placing a more reactive metal with the iron. The water and oxygen react with this 'sacrificial' metal instead of with the object you're protecting.

5) Galvanising is an example of sacrificial protection, where a coat of zinc is put onto an iron object to prevent rusting. The zinc acts as sacrificial protection — it's more reactive than iron, so it'll lose electrons and corrode in preference to iron. The zinc also acts as a barrier. Steel buckets and corrugated iron roofing are often galvanised.

Electroplating is Applying a Metal Coating to an Object

1) Electroplating is coating the surface of a metal with another metal using electrolysis.

2) The cathode is the object you're going to electroplate, the anode is the bar of metal you're using for the plating. Your electrolyte is a solution containing the metal ions of the metal you're using for the plating.

3) Electroplating is really useful. Household objects like cutlery and cooking utensils are electroplated with metals to stop them corroding. The metals used for protection are unreactive and don't corrode easily.

4) Jewellery and decorative items are often electroplated with metals like gold or silver. This improves the appearance of the metals — making them look shiny and attractive.

Example: Electroplating silver onto a brass cup.

- The cathode is the brass cup and the anode is a bar of pure silver.
- The electrolyte is silver nitrate solution ($AgNO_3$).
- The silver ions from the electrolyte move towards the cathode and metal gets deposited on the brass cup. The anode keeps the silver ions in the solution 'topped up'.

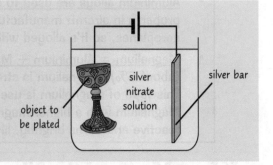
object to be plated
silver nitrate solution
silver bar

Cathode: $Ag^+ + e^- \rightarrow Ag$ 　　Anode: $Ag \rightarrow Ag^+ + e^-$

My old robot friend died yesterday — may he rust in peace...

Rust gets everywhere. On my car, my old bike, now in your exam. Best get some practice in now...

Q1　　Outline how bolting some magnesium onto a piece of iron will prevent it from rusting.　　[2 marks]

Titrations

Titrations are full of big, fancy bits of glass — so they're bad for clumsy people (like me)...

Titrations are Used to Find Out Concentrations

PRACTICAL

1) Titrations allow you to find out <u>exactly</u> how much acid is needed to <u>neutralise</u> a given quantity of alkali (or vice versa).

2) Using a <u>pipette</u>, measure out a set volume of the <u>alkali</u> into a flask. Add a few drops of an <u>indicator</u> — usually <u>phenolphthalein</u> or <u>methyl orange</u> (see p.43).
You can't use Universal indicator — it changes colour gradually and you want a single colour change.

3) Fill a <u>burette</u> with a <u>standard solution</u> (a <u>known concentration</u>) of acid.
Keep the burette below eye level while you fill it — you don't want to be looking up if any acid spills.

4) Use the burette to add the acid to the alkali a bit at a time. <u>Swirl</u> the flask regularly. Go <u>slowly</u> (a drop at a time) when you think the alkali's almost neutralised.
To work out when this is, do a rough titration first. Don't worry about recording the exact end point first time, just note the approximate amount of acid you need, then go slowly as you get near this amount on the next runs. Doing your titration with your flask standing on a white tile will make the colour changes easier to see too.

5) The indicator <u>changes colour</u> when <u>all</u> the alkali has been <u>neutralised</u> — phenolphthalein is <u>pink</u> in <u>alkalis</u> but <u>colourless</u> in <u>acids</u>, and methyl orange is <u>yellow</u> in <u>alkalis</u> but <u>red</u> in <u>acids</u>.

6) <u>Record</u> the <u>volume</u> of acid used to <u>neutralise</u> the alkali (called the <u>titre</u>).

7) <u>Repeat</u> this process a few times, making sure you get <u>very similar</u> results each time. You can then take the <u>mean</u> (see page 7) of your results.

For more on how to use burettes and pipettes, see page 109.

Burette containing standard solution of acid.

The scale down the side shows the volume of acid used.

Alkali and indicator.

You Can Calculate the Concentration Using Your Titration Results

1) The <u>concentration</u> of a solution can be measured in <u>moles per dm³</u> — so 1 mole of a substance dissolved in 1 dm³ of solution has a concentration of <u>1 mole per dm³</u> (or 1 mol dm⁻³). (Concentration can also be measured in g dm⁻³ — see page 29 for more.)

2) The formula for <u>concentration</u> in <u>mol dm⁻³</u> is similar to the one for g dm⁻³:

> **concentration = number of moles ÷ volume of solution**

3) You can use the results of a <u>titration experiment</u> to calculate the concentration of the alkali when you know the concentration of the acid (or vice versa).

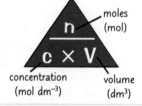

moles (mol)

concentration (mol dm⁻³)

volume (dm³)

EXAMPLE:

It takes 25.0 cm³ of 0.100 mol dm⁻³ sulfuric acid to neutralise 30.0 cm³ of sodium hydroxide solution. The equation for this reaction is: $2NaOH + H_2SO_4 \rightarrow Na_2SO_4 + 2H_2O$
Find the concentration of the alkali in mol dm⁻³.

1) Work out how many <u>moles</u> of acid you have, using the formula: moles = concentration × volume.
moles = 0.100 × (25.0 ÷ 1000)
= 0.00250 moles of H_2SO_4

Convert the volume into dm³. (1000 cm³ = 1 dm³)

2) Use the equation to work out how many <u>moles</u> of the alkali you must have had, using the ratios in the balanced equation.
1 mole of H_2SO_4 reacts with 2 moles of NaOH
So 0.00250 moles of H_2SO_4 must react with
0.00250 × 2 = 0.00500 moles of NaOH

3) Finally, work out the <u>concentration</u> of the alkali.
concentration = number of moles ÷ volume
= 0.00500 ÷ (30.0 ÷ 1000)
= 0.1666... mol dm⁻³ = **0.167 mol dm⁻³**

Again, convert the volume into dm³.

4) You might also need to convert a concentration in mol dm⁻³ into g dm⁻³. To do this, multiply the concentration in mol dm⁻³ by the <u>relative formula mass</u> of the solute.
For the example above, M_r of NaOH = 23 + 16 + 1 = 40
So, the concentration of the solution in g dm⁻³ = 0.166... × 40 = 6.666... g dm⁻³ = **6.7 g dm⁻³**.

To convert from g dm⁻³ to mol dm⁻³, divide by the M_r.

Titration calculations require maths and concentration...

Holy moley, what a lot of numbers. Have a peek at page 109 if you want more details about using a burette.

Q1 27 cm³ of 0.50 mol dm⁻³ hydrochloric acid neutralises 15 cm³ of sodium hydroxide solution. The equation is: $HCl + NaOH \rightarrow NaCl + H_2O$. Find the concentration of the sodium hydroxide in mol dm⁻³. [4 marks]

Percentage Yield

Percentage yield compares the amount of product you should get with what you actually get.

Percentage Yield Compares Actual and Theoretical Yield

1) The amount of product you get from a reaction is known as the yield. The more reactants you start with, the higher the actual yield will be — that's pretty obvious. But the percentage yield doesn't depend on the amount of reactants you started with — it's a percentage. Percentage yield is given by the formula:

$$\text{Percentage yield} = \frac{\text{actual yield}}{\text{theoretical yield}} \times 100$$

The theoretical yield is sometimes called the predicted yield.

2) The theoretical yield of a reaction is the mass of product you'd make if all the reactants were converted to products. Theoretical yield can be calculated from the balanced reaction equation (see page 31).

EXAMPLE:

In an industrial reaction, iron oxide reacts with carbon to make iron:

$$2Fe_2O_3 + 3C \rightarrow 4Fe + 3CO_2$$

Calculate the percentage yield if you started with 50 kg of iron oxide and produced 18.9 kg of iron.

1) Find the relative formula mass of iron oxide and the relative atomic mass of iron.

$M_r(Fe_2O_3) = (2 \times 56) + (3 \times 16) = 160$
$A_r(Fe) = 56$

2) Work out the number of moles of the reactant (iron oxide) you have.

moles of Fe_2O_3 = mass ÷ M_r
= $(50 \times 1000) \div 160$
= $50\,000 \div 160 = 312.5$ moles

Convert the mass to grams: 1 kg = 1000 g

3) Use the balanced chemical equation to work out how many moles of the desired product (iron) you should end up with.

The equation tells you that 2 moles of iron oxide produces 4 moles of iron. So 312.5 moles of iron oxide should produce $(312.5 \div 2) \times 4 = 625$ moles of iron.

4) Work out the theoretical yield of your desired product (iron) by converting this number of moles into mass.

mass = moles × A_r
= 625×56
= $35\,000$ g = 35 kg

Make sure your theoretical yield and your actual yield are in the same units.

5) Finally, pop the numbers into the formula to find the percentage yield.

percentage yield = $\frac{\text{actual yield}}{\text{theoretical yield}} \times 100$
= $\frac{18.9}{35} \times 100 = 54\%$

3) Percentage yield is always somewhere between 0 and 100%. A 100% percentage yield means that you got all the product you expected to get. A 0% yield means that no product was made at all.

4) In a reaction with a low percentage yield, a lot of the reactants will be wasted. In industry it's important to use reactions with the highest yield possible to reduce waste and keep costs as low as possible.

In real life, you never get a 100% yield. There are a number of ways this can happen, for example:

- Incomplete reactions — if not all of the reactants are converted to product, the reaction is incomplete and the yield will be lower than expected.

- Practical losses — you always lose a bit when you transfer chemicals between containers. Imagine pouring a liquid into a new container — some is always left on the inside surface of the old container.

- Unwanted reactions — if unexpected reactions happen, the yield of the intended product goes down. These can be caused by impurities in the reactants, or sometimes by changes to the reaction conditions.

There are 10 grams of virtual soil in my theoretical field...

It may seem like a load of numbers, but percentage yield is really important in industry.

Q1 1.62 g of silver were made from 3.48 g of silver(I) oxide during the following reaction:
$2Ag_2O \rightarrow 4Ag + O_2$. What is the percentage yield of the reaction? [4 marks]

Atom Economy

It's important in <u>industrial reactions</u> that as much of the reactants as possible get turned into <u>useful products</u>. This depends on the <u>atom economy</u> and the <u>percentage yield</u> (see previous page) of the reaction.

Atom Economy is the % of Reactants Changed to Useful Products

1) A lot of reactions make <u>more than one product</u>. Some of them will be <u>useful</u>, but others will just be <u>waste</u>.

2) The <u>atom economy</u> of a reaction tells you what percentage of the <u>mass of the reactants</u> has been converted into your <u>desired product</u> when manufacturing a chemical. Here's the formula:

$$\text{Atom Economy} = \frac{\text{total } M_r \text{ of desired products}}{\text{total } M_r \text{ of all products}} \times 100$$

3) <u>100%</u> atom economy means that <u>all</u> the atoms in the reactants have been turned into <u>useful</u> (desired) <u>products</u>. The <u>higher</u> the atom economy the '<u>greener</u>' the process.

 Hydrogen gas can be made industrially by reacting natural gas (methane) with steam.

$$CH_{4\,(g)} + H_2O_{(g)} \rightarrow CO_{(g)} + 3H_{2\,(g)}$$

Calculate the atom economy of this reaction. Give your answer to 2 significant figures.

1) Identify the <u>desired product</u>.

   The desired product is hydrogen gas (H_2).

2) Work out the total M_r of <u>all the products</u>.

   M_r of all products = $M_r(CO) + [3 \times M_r(H_2)]$
   $= (12 + 16) + [3 \times (2 \times 1)] = 28 + 6 = 34$

3) Then work out the total M_r of just the <u>desired products</u>.

   M_r of desired products = $3 \times M_r(H_2) = 3 \times (2 \times 1) = 6$

4) Use the formula to calculate the <u>atom economy</u>.

   Atom economy = $\dfrac{\text{total } M_r \text{ of desired products}}{\text{total } M_r \text{ of all products}} \times 100$

   $= \dfrac{6}{34} \times 100 = \mathbf{18\%}$

So in this reaction, 82% of the starting materials are wasted.

High Atom Economy is Better for Profits and the Environment

1) Reactions with low atom economies <u>use up resources</u> very quickly. At the same time, they make lots of <u>waste</u> materials that have to be <u>disposed</u> of somehow. That tends to make these reactions <u>unsustainable</u> — the raw materials will run out and the waste has to go somewhere.

2) For the same reasons, low atom economy reactions aren't usually <u>profitable</u>. Raw materials can be <u>expensive to buy</u> and waste products can be expensive to <u>remove</u> and dispose of <u>responsibly</u>.

3) One way around the problem is to find a <u>use</u> for the waste products rather than just <u>throwing them away</u>. There's often <u>more than one way</u> to make the product you want — so the trick is to come up with a reaction that gives <u>useful 'by-products'</u> rather than useless ones.

4) Atom economy isn't the only factor to consider in <u>industry</u>. You also need to think about:

   • The <u>percentage yield</u> (see last page) of the reaction — the higher the yield the better.

   • The <u>rate of reaction</u> (see page 77) — the rate of the reaction you're using must be <u>fast enough</u> to produce the amount of product you need in a sensible amount of time.

   • If your reaction's <u>reversible</u> (see page 59). To keep the <u>yield</u> of a reversible reaction high, you might need to alter the <u>equilibrium position</u> by changing <u>reaction conditions</u> (which can be <u>expensive</u>).

Atom economy — budget travel for chemists...

High atom economy = yay! High yield = yay! Useful by-products = yay! Some practice questions = ???

Q1 What is the atom economy of the following reaction, used to make hydrogen?

$$C_{(s)} + 2H_2O_{(g)} \rightarrow CO_{2\,(g)} + 2H_{2\,(g)}$$ [4 marks]

Q2 Give two reasons why a high atom economy is important in industrial reactions. [2 marks]

The Haber Process

You need to know why we use the <u>conditions</u> we use for a certain industrial reaction. Can't be too hard... can it?

The Reaction Conditions Used in Industrial Processes are a Compromise

1) When you're designing an <u>industrial process</u>, there are a number of factors to consider.

2) The <u>cost</u> of extracting and refining the <u>raw materials</u> will affect whether the process is <u>economically viable</u> or not. If the raw materials are <u>too expensive</u> to source, it may not be <u>profitable</u> to make the product.

3) <u>Energy costs</u> (costs associated with <u>reaching</u> and <u>maintaining</u> the <u>conditions</u> required for the reaction, e.g. <u>temperature</u> and <u>pressure</u>) also affect whether a reaction is profitable. Generally, high temperatures and pressures cost more to maintain, so <u>low temperatures</u> and <u>pressures</u> are used wherever possible.

4) It's important to be able to <u>control the conditions</u> (the temperature, pressure and the presence of a catalyst) to <u>maximise your yield</u>, but keep your reaction running at an <u>acceptable rate</u>.

Example: the Conditions Used in the Haber Process

The <u>Haber process</u> produces <u>ammonia</u> using the following reaction:

$$N_{2\,(g)} + 3H_{2\,(g)} \rightleftharpoons 2NH_{3\,(g)} \quad (+ \text{ heat})$$

> You met the Haber process on page 59.

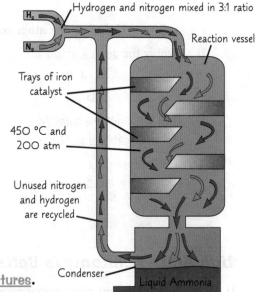

Hydrogen and nitrogen mixed in 3:1 ratio

Reaction vessel

Trays of iron catalyst

450 °C and 200 atm

Unused nitrogen and hydrogen are recycled

Condenser

Liquid Ammonia

1) <u>Higher pressures</u> favour the <u>forward</u> reaction (since there are four moles of gas on the left-hand side, for every two moles on the right — see the equation above).

2) So the pressure is set <u>as high as possible</u> to give the best yield (see page 66), without making the plant too expensive to build (e.g. it'd be too expensive to build a plant that'd stand pressures of over 1000 atmospheres). So, the operating pressure is <u>200 atmospheres</u>.

3) The <u>forward reaction</u> is <u>exothermic</u>, which means that <u>increasing</u> the <u>temperature</u> will actually move the equilibrium position the <u>wrong way</u> — away from ammonia and towards nitrogen and hydrogen. So the yield of ammonia would be greater at <u>lower temperatures</u>.

4) The trouble is, <u>lower temperatures</u> mean a <u>lower rate of reaction</u>. So in industry, the temperature is increased anyway, to get a much faster rate of reaction.

5) The 450 °C is a <u>compromise</u> between <u>maximum yield</u> and <u>speed of reaction</u>. It's better to wait just <u>20 seconds</u> for a <u>10% yield</u> than to have to wait <u>60 seconds</u> for a <u>20% yield</u>.

Catalysts and Conditions Both Affect How Quickly Equilibrium is Reached

1) The <u>temperature</u>, <u>pressure</u> and <u>concentration</u> of reactants also affect how quickly <u>equilibrium</u> is reached. If you increase the <u>rate of reaction</u> (see p.77), you also increase the <u>rate</u> at which you reach <u>equilibrium</u>.

2) So equilibrium is always reached <u>faster</u> using <u>high</u> temperatures, <u>high</u> pressures and <u>high</u> concentrations (but remember, depending on the reaction, using these conditions could decrease <u>yield</u>).

3) Catalysts are useful too. For example, in the Haber process, the <u>iron catalyst</u> makes the reaction go <u>faster</u>, so it reaches <u>equilibrium</u> faster too. But the catalyst <u>doesn't</u> affect the <u>position</u> of equilibrium, or the % yield.

> Without the catalyst, the Haber process would have to be carried out at an even higher temperature in order to get a quick enough reaction — and that would reduce the % yield of ammonia even further. So the catalyst is very important.

It's tricky stuff but go on, Haber go at it...

Look back at page 60 if you need a reminder on how changing reaction conditions affects equilibrium and yield.

Q1   A pressure of 200 atm is used in the industrial production of ammonia via the Haber process. What would happen to the yield of ammonia if a higher pressure was used? Explain your answer.   [2 marks]

Fertilisers

There's a lot more to using <u>fertilisers</u> than making your garden look nice and pretty...

Fertilisers Help Plants Grow

1) The three main <u>essential</u> elements in fertilisers are <u>nitrogen</u>, <u>phosphorus</u> and <u>potassium</u>. Plants absorb these nutrients from the soil.

2) If plants don't get enough of these elements, their <u>growth</u> and <u>life processes</u> are affected.

3) Fertilisers <u>supply</u> these elements if they're missing from the soil, or provide <u>more</u> of them. This helps to increase the <u>crop yield</u>, as the crops can grow <u>faster</u> and <u>bigger</u>.

4) Ammonia fertilisers have some important <u>advantages</u> compared to <u>traditional fertilisers</u>, like manure. You can <u>control</u> the <u>compositions of chemicals</u> in them, as well as <u>how much</u> is made. Ammonia fertilisers are also <u>soluble</u>, so all the chemicals can <u>dissolve</u> down into the soil to reach the plants.

Ammonia is Used to Produce Nitrogen-Containing Compounds

1) Ammonia can be reacted with oxygen and water in a series of reactions to make <u>nitric acid</u>.

2) You can also react ammonia with acids, <u>including</u> nitric acid and phosphoric acid, to get <u>ammonium salts</u>.

3) For example, ammonia and nitric acid react together to produce the salt <u>ammonium nitrate</u> — a fertiliser: $NH_{3\,(aq)} + HNO_{3\,(aq)} \rightarrow NH_4NO_{3\,(aq)}$

Different Methods are Used to Prepare Ammonium Sulfate

<u>Ammonium sulfate</u> is a fertiliser you can make in the lab. You'll need <u>ammonia</u> and <u>dilute sulfuric acid</u>. You can make most fertilisers using this <u>titration</u> method — just choose the right <u>acid</u> (nitric, sulfuric or phosphoric) and <u>alkali</u> (ammonia or potassium hydroxide) to get the <u>salt</u> you want.

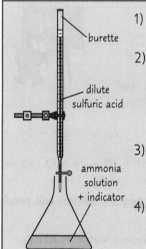

burette

dilute sulfuric acid

ammonia solution + indicator

See page 65 for more on titrations.

1) Set up your apparatus as in the diagram. Add a few drops of <u>methyl orange indicator</u> to the ammonia — it'll turn <u>yellow</u>.

2) <u>Slowly</u> add the dilute sulfuric acid from the burette into the ammonia, until the yellow colour <u>just</u> changes to red. Gently swirl the flask as you add the acid. Go especially <u>slowly</u> when you get close to the end point. Methyl orange is <u>yellow</u> in <u>alkalis</u>, but <u>red</u> in <u>acids</u>, so this <u>colour change</u> means that <u>all</u> the ammonia has been <u>neutralised</u> and you've got ammonium sulfate solution.

3) The ammonium sulfate solution isn't <u>pure</u> — it's still got <u>methyl orange</u> in it. To get <u>pure</u> ammonium sulfate crystals, you need to note <u>exactly</u> how much sulfuric acid it took to neutralise the ammonia, then repeat the titration using that volume of acid, but <u>no indicator</u>.

4) To get solid <u>ammonium sulfate crystals</u>, gently evaporate the solution (using a steam bath) until only a little bit is left. Leave it to <u>crystallise</u> then filter out the crystals and leave them to dry (see page 38).

1) The method above isn't used to make ammonium sulfate in <u>industry</u>. It's <u>impractical</u> to use burettes and steam baths for large quantities, and using crystallisation to get solid ammonium sulfate is <u>too slow</u>.

2) The industrial production of ammonium sulfate usually has <u>several stages</u>, as the ammonia and sulfuric acid have to be made from their <u>raw materials</u> first. <u>Ammonia</u> is made using the <u>Haber process</u> (see last page), and <u>sulfuric acid</u> is produced using a process called the <u>Contact process</u>.

3) One industrial method uses a large reaction chamber filled with <u>ammonia gas</u>. Sulfuric acid is <u>sprayed</u> into the reaction chamber, where it reacts with the ammonia to produce ammonium sulfate powder.

That titration reminds me of my car — it's the orange indicators...

Yet another titration... It's pretty similar to the one you met back on page 65, so no need to panic.

Q1 What is the role of a fertiliser? [1 mark]

Q2 Describe the process for making pure ammonium sulfate crystals in the lab. [6 marks]

Calculations with Gases

With <u>gases</u>, it's easier to use <u>volume</u> instead of <u>concentration</u>. Time to meet my old friend the <u>molar volume</u>...

Molar Volume is the Volume Occupied by One Mole of Gas

1) The volume occupied by <u>one mole of a gas</u> is known as the <u>molar volume</u>.

2) It usually has units of <u>dm³ mol⁻¹</u> (dm³ per mole).

3) Here's <u>formula</u> for calculating <u>molar volume</u>:

$$\text{molar volume} = \text{gas volume} \div \text{number of moles}$$

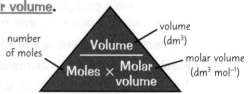

EXAMPLE: Under certain conditions, 0.050 moles of nitrogen gas, N_2, was found to occupy 1.4 dm³. What is the molar volume of nitrogen in dm³ mol⁻¹ under these conditions?

Substitute the moles and volume into the equation for the <u>molar volume</u>.

molar volume = volume ÷ number of moles
= 1.4 ÷ 0.050 = **28 dm³ mol⁻¹**

Molar Volumes are the Same Under the Same Conditions

<u>Avogadro's law</u> states that under the <u>same conditions</u>, the <u>same number of moles</u> of different gases all occupy the <u>same volume</u>.

> One mole of any gas always occupies 24 dm³ (= 24 000 cm³) at room temperature and pressure (RTP = 20 °C and 1 atmosphere).

So, at RTP, all gases have the same <u>molar volume</u> — 24 dm³ mol⁻¹.

In the exam, you'll be given the value of the molar volume at RTP if you need it.

EXAMPLE: What's the volume of 4.50 moles of chlorine at RTP?

1 mole = 24 dm³, so 4.50 moles = 4.50 × 24 dm³ = **108 dm³**

EXAMPLE: How many moles are there in 8280 cm³ of hydrogen gas at RTP?

1) Make sure everything is in the <u>right units</u>. You need to convert the volume into dm³.

1000 cm³ = 1 dm³
So, 8280 cm³ = 8280 ÷ 1000 = 8.28 dm³

2) <u>Rearrange the formula</u> linking volume, number of moles and molar volume (24 dm³) to get <u>number of moles</u> on its own.

Number of moles = volume of gas ÷ 24

3) Substitute your values into the rearranged equation.

Number of moles = 8.28 ÷ 24 = **0.345 moles**

You can use Avogadro's law with a <u>balanced equation</u> to work out the <u>volume of gas</u> a reaction will produce.

EXAMPLE: How much gas is produced when 11.5 g of sodium is reacted with excess water at RTP?

$$2Na_{(s)} + 2H_2O_{(l)} \rightarrow 2NaOH_{(aq)} + H_{2\,(g)}$$

1) Find the <u>number of moles of Na</u> used.

A_r of Na = 23, so 11.5 g of Na = 11.5 ÷ 23 = 0.50 moles

2) Use the <u>balanced equation</u> to find the number of moles of H_2 this will produce.

From the equation, 2 moles of Na produce 1 mole of H_2, so you know 0.50 moles Na produces 0.50 ÷ 2 = 0.25 moles H_2.

3) Use the <u>formula</u> to find the volume of 0.25 moles of gas.

So the volume of H_2 = 0.25 × 24 = **6.0 dm³**

Memoirs of a Tooth Fairy — my favourite molar volume...

Don't let molar volumes ruin your life — make sure you can use and rearrange the formula, and all will be fine.

Q1 2.4 g of argon gas (Ar) takes up a volume of 1.32 dm³. What is the molar volume of argon under these conditions? [2 marks]

Q2 The M_r of methane (CH_4) is 16. What volume will 36 g of methane gas occupy at RTP? [2 marks]

Fuel Cells

Fuel cells are great — and the one you need to know about is particularly great in my opinion. The hydrogen-oxygen fuel cell uses hydrogen and oxygen to make electricity. I bet you're dying to find out more...

Fuel Cells Use Fuel and Oxygen to Produce Electrical Energy

1) Chemical cells produce a voltage across the cell, until all of one of the reactants has been used up.

2) A fuel cell is a type of chemical cell that's supplied with a fuel and oxygen and uses energy from the reaction between them to produce electrical energy efficiently.

3) There are a few different types of fuel cells, using different fuels and different electrolytes.

Hydrogen-Oxygen Fuel Cells use Hydrogen as a Fuel

1) The reaction between hydrogen and oxygen releases energy.

2) This is what happens in a hydrogen-oxygen fuel cell — you can produce a voltage (i.e. electrical energy) by reacting hydrogen and oxygen, and it doesn't produce any nasty pollutants, only nice clean water...

3) The overall reaction is:

$$\text{hydrogen} + \text{oxygen} \rightarrow \text{water}$$
$$2H_2 + O_2 \rightarrow 2H_2O$$

Hydrogen-Oxygen Fuel Cells Have Lots of Advantages

1) Hydrogen fuel cells are great — they're much more efficient than power stations or batteries at producing electricity. If you use the heat produced as well, their efficiency can be greater than 80%.

2) In a fuel cell, the electricity is generated directly from the reaction (so no turbines, generators, etc.).

3) Because there aren't a lot of stages to the process of generating electricity there are fewer places for energy to be lost as heat.

4) Unlike a car engine or a fossil fuel burning power station, there are no moving parts, so energy isn't lost through friction.

5) Fuel cell vehicles don't produce any conventional pollutants — no greenhouse gases, no nitrogen oxides, no sulfur dioxide, no carbon monoxide. The only by-products are water and heat. This would be a major advantage in cities, where air pollution from traffic is a big problem.

This could mean no more smelly petrol and diesel cars, lorries and buses. It could also replace batteries — which are incredibly polluting to dispose of because they're usually made of highly toxic metal compounds.

See page 89 for more on pollutants.

However, it's not likely to mean the end of either conventional power stations or our dependence on fossil fuels. That's because:

- hydrogen is a gas so it takes up loads more space to store than liquid fuels like petrol.
- it's very explosive so it's difficult to store safely.
- the hydrogen fuel is often made either from hydrocarbons (from fossil fuels), or by electrolysis of water, which uses electricity (and that electricity's got to be generated somehow — usually this involves fossil fuels).

A fuel cell — prison for disobedient petrolheads...

If you want to know more about all the nasty stuff conventional engines spew out, have a look at page 89.

Q1   Write out the overall reaction that occurs in a hydrogen-oxygen fuel cell.   [1 mark]

Q2   Give one advantage and one disadvantage of using fuel cells for energy.   [2 marks]

Revision Questions for Topic 5

So, now you know everything there is to know about how useful chemistry can be in the real world.
Okay, maybe not everything... But you should know enough to answer these Revision Questions.

- Try these questions and <u>tick off each one</u> when you <u>get it right</u>.
- When you've done <u>all the questions</u> under a heading and are <u>completely happy</u> with it, tick it off.

Transition Metals, Alloys and Corrosion (p.62-64) ☑

1) Give two examples of transition metals. ☑
2) a) Give two properties transition metals have in common with most other metals. ☑
   b) Give two typical properties of transition metals that they don't share with most other metals. ☑
3) What is an alloy? ☑
4) Explain why alloys are usually stronger than pure metals. ☑
5) What element is added to iron to make steel? ☑
6) Give one use of: a) bronze,   b) brass,   c) magnalium. ☑
7) Why is rusting a redox reaction? ☑
8) Give two ways rusting can be prevented. ☑
9) Give the two main reasons why an object might be electroplated. ☑

Quantitative Analysis (p.65-67) ☑

10) Why is Universal indicator not used during titrations? ☑
11) At the start of a titration experiment, phenolphthalein was added to an acidic solution.
    What colour change would you see when the acid had been completely neutralised? ☑
12) What's the formula for calculating the concentration of a solution in mol dm^{-3}? ☑
13) State the formula for the percentage yield of a reaction. ☑
14) What does the term 'theoretical yield' mean? ☑
15) What does it mean if the percentage yield of a reaction is 100%? ☑
16) Explain why the percentage yield of a reaction is always less than 100% in real life. ☑
17) What formula would you use to work out the atom economy of a reaction? ☑
18) Why aren't reactions with low atom economies usually profitable? ☑

The Haber Process and Fertilisers (p.68-69) ☑

19) What chemical is manufactured using the Haber Process? ☑
20) Explain why the conditions used in the Haber Process are a compromise between rate and yield. ☑
21) Suggest three ways that you could increase the rate of attainment of equilibrium. ☑
22) Give two examples of compounds that are used as fertilisers. ☑
23) Briefly outline the main stages that are involved in the industrial production of ammonium sulfate. ☑

Volumes of Gases (p.70) ☑

24) What is the 'molar volume' of a gas? ☑
25) What volume does one mole of gas occupy at room temperature and pressure? ☑

Fuel Cells (p.71) ☑

26) What is the only product of the reaction in a hydrogen-oxygen fuel cell? ☑
27) Explain why it's unlikely that hydrogen-oxygen fuels cells will replace conventional power stations. ☑

Group 1 — Alkali Metals

You can predict how different elements will <u>react</u> by looking at where they are in the <u>periodic table</u> — elements in the <u>same group</u> will react in <u>similar ways</u>. Time to take a look at some of the groups, starting with <u>Group 1</u>...

Group 1 Metals are Known as the 'Alkali Metals'

The <u>Group 1</u> metals are lithium, sodium, potassium, rubidium, caesium and francium.

1) The alkali metals all have <u>one outer electron</u>
   — so they have <u>similar chemical properties</u>.

2) They all have the following <u>physical properties</u>:
   - <u>Low melting points</u> and <u>boiling points</u> (compared with other metals).
   - <u>Very soft</u> — they can be cut with a knife.

3) The alkali metals form <u>ionic</u> compounds. They lose their single outer electron <u>so easily</u> that sharing it is out of the question, so they <u>don't</u> form covalent bonds.

Group 1	Group 2	
7 Li Lithium 3	Be	
23 Na Sodium 11	Mg	
39 K Potassium 19	Ca	Sc
86 Rb Rubidium 37	Sr	Y
133 Cs Caesium 55	Ba	
223 Fr Francium 87	Ra	

Group 1 Metals are Very Reactive

1) The Group 1 metals readily <u>lose</u> their single <u>outer electron</u> to form a <u>1+ ion</u> with a <u>stable electronic structure</u>.

2) The <u>more readily</u> a metal loses its outer electrons, the <u>more reactive</u> it is — so the Group 1 metals are very reactive.

3) As you go <u>down</u> Group 1, the alkali metals get <u>more reactive</u>. The <u>outer electron</u> is more easily <u>lost</u> because it's further from the nucleus (the <u>atomic radius</u> is <u>larger</u>) — so it's less strongly attracted to the nucleus and <u>less energy</u> is needed to remove it.

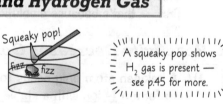

$$Li \rightarrow Li^+ + e^-$$

Reactions with Cold Water Produces a Hydroxide and Hydrogen Gas

1) When the <u>alkali metals</u> are put in <u>water</u>, they react <u>vigorously</u>.

2) The reaction produces <u>hydrogen gas</u> and a <u>hydroxide</u> of the metal (an <u>alkali</u> see page 43). For example, here's the overall equation for the reaction of <u>sodium</u> with <u>water</u>:

Squeaky pop!

fizz fizz

A squeaky pop shows H_2 gas is present — see p.45 for more.

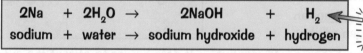

$$2Na + 2H_2O \rightarrow 2NaOH + H_2$$

sodium + water → sodium hydroxide + hydrogen

The same reaction happens with all of the alkali metals — make sure you can write balanced equations for them all.

3) The reactivity of Group 1 metals with water (and dilute acid) <u>increases down the group</u> because the outer electron is lost more easily in the reaction (see above). This results in the reaction becoming <u>more violent</u>:
   - <u>Lithium</u> will <u>move</u> around the surface, <u>fizzing</u> furiously.
   - <u>Sodium</u> and <u>potassium</u> do the same, but they also <u>melt</u> in the heat of the reaction. Potassium even gets hot enough to <u>ignite</u> the hydrogen gas being produced.

4) Because you know the <u>reactivity trend</u> in Group 1 (the elements get more reactive as you go down the group), you can make <u>predictions</u> about the reactions of elements further down the group.

> <u>Example:</u> You may predict that the reactions of rubidium and caesium with water will be <u>more violent</u> than the reaction of potassium and water. And sure enough, <u>rubidium</u> and <u>caesium</u> react <u>violently</u> with water and tend to <u>explode</u> when they get wet...

And that's why you don't get caesium teaspoons... Amongst other reasons...

Alkali metals are so reactive, in fact, that they have to be stored in oil — otherwise they just react with the air.

Q1 A student reacts lithium with water. Describe what the student will observe. [1 mark]

Q2 Write a balanced symbol equation for the reaction between potassium (K) and water. [2 marks]

Group 7 — Halogens

Here's a page on another periodic table group that you need to be familiar with — the halogens.

Group 7 Elements are Known as the 'Halogens'

Group 7 is made up of the elements fluorine, chlorine, bromine, iodine and astatine.

1) All Group 7 elements have 7 electrons in their outer shell so they all have similar chemical properties.

2) The halogens exist as diatomic molecules (e.g. Cl_2, Br_2, I_2). Sharing one pair of electrons in a covalent bond (see page 23) gives both atoms a full outer shell.

3) As you go down Group 7, the melting points and boiling points of the halogens increase. This means that at room temperature:
   - Chlorine (Cl_2) is a fairly reactive, poisonous, green gas.
   - Bromine (Br_2) is a poisonous, red-brown liquid, which gives off an orange vapour at room temperature.
   - Iodine (I_2) is a dark grey crystalline solid which gives off a purple vapour when heated.

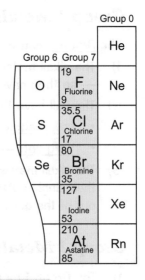

	Group 6	Group 7	Group 0
			He
	O	19 F Fluorine 9	Ne
	S	35.5 Cl Chlorine 17	Ar
	Se	80 Br Bromine 35	Kr
		127 I Iodine 53	Xe
		210 At Astatine 85	Rn

You can use the trends in physical properties from chlorine to iodine to predict the properties of halogens further down the group. For example, you can see that melting point increases down the group, and the colours of the halogens get darker, so you could predict that astatine (which comes below iodine) would be a dark-coloured solid at room temperature.

Test for Chlorine Using Damp Blue Litmus Paper

You can test to see if a gas is chlorine by holding a piece of damp blue litmus paper over it. Chlorine will bleach the litmus paper, turning it white. It may also turn red for a moment first — that's because a solution of chlorine is acidic (see p.43 for more on acids).

damp blue litmus paper

chlorine

Reactivity Decreases Going Down Group 7

1) A halogen atom only needs to gain one electron to form a 1– ion with a stable electronic structure.

$$Cl + e^- \rightarrow Cl^-$$

2) The easier it is for a halogen atom to attract an electron, the more reactive the halogen will be.

3) As you go down Group 7, the halogens become less reactive — it gets harder to attract the extra electron to fill the outer shell when it's further away from the nucleus (the atomic radius is larger).

The Halogens Can React With Metals and Hydrogen

1) The halogens will react vigorously with some metals to form salts called 'metal halides'.

$$2Na + Cl_2 \rightarrow 2NaCl$$
$$\text{Sodium} + \text{Chlorine} \rightarrow \text{Sodium chloride}$$

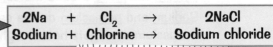
Metals lose electrons and form positive ions when they react.

2) Halogens higher up in Group 7 are more reactive because they can attract the outer electron of the metal more easily.

3) Halogens can also react with hydrogen to form hydrogen halides. Hydrogen halides are soluble, and they can dissolve in water to form acidic solutions. For example, HCl forms hydrochloric acid in water.

$$H_2 + Cl_2 \rightarrow 2HCl$$
$$\text{Hydrogen} + \text{Chlorine} \rightarrow \text{Hydrogen chloride}$$

4) Since all halogens have the same number of electrons in their outer shells, they all have similar reactions. So you can use the reactions of chlorine, bromine and iodine to predict how fluorine and astatine will react.

Halogens — one electron short of a full shell...

Another page, another periodic table group to learn the properties and the trends of. It's like Christmas come early.

Q1   Write a balanced symbol equation for the reaction between bromine (Br_2) and sodium (Na).   [2 marks]

Halogen Displacement Reactions

The halogens are a pretty competitive lot really. In fact the <u>more reactive</u> ones will push the <u>less reactive</u> ones out of a compound. How uncivilized — has nobody ever taught them that it's bad manners to push?

A More Reactive Halogen Will Displace a Less Reactive One

1) The elements in Group 7 take part in <u>displacement reactions</u>.

2) A <u>displacement reaction</u> is where a <u>more reactive</u> element 'pushes out' (<u>displaces</u>) a <u>less reactive</u> element from a compound.

3) The halogen displacement reactions are <u>redox</u> reactions. The halogens <u>gain electrons</u> (reduction) whilst halide ions <u>lose electrons</u> (oxidation).

4) For example, <u>chlorine</u> is more reactive than <u>bromine</u> (it's higher up Group 7). If you add <u>chlorine water</u> (an <u>aqueous solution</u> of Cl_2) to <u>potassium bromide</u> solution, the chlorine will <u>displace</u> the <u>bromine</u> from the salt solution.

5) The <u>chlorine</u> is reduced to <u>chloride ions</u>, so the salt solution becomes <u>potassium chloride</u>. The <u>bromide ions</u> are oxidised to <u>bromine</u>, which turns the solution <u>orange</u>.

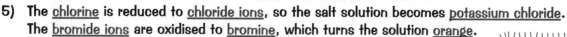

Cl_2	+	2KBr	$\rightarrow$	Br_2	+	2KCl
chlorine	+	potassium bromide	$\rightarrow$	bromine	+	potassium chloride

Cl_2	+	$2Br^-$	$\rightarrow$	Br_2	+	$2Cl^-$
chlorine	+	bromide ions	$\rightarrow$	bromine	+	chloride ions

All equations for halogen displacement reactions follow this pattern.

You can see the loss and gain of electrons by looking at the ionic equation.

Displacement Reactions Show Reactivity Trends

You can use <u>displacement reactions</u> to show the reactivity trend of the halogens.

1) Start by measuring out a small amount of a <u>halide salt solution</u> in a test tube.

2) Add a few drops of a <u>halogen solution</u> to it and shake the tube gently.

3) If you see a <u>colour change</u>, then a reaction has happened — the halogen has displaced the halide ions from the salt. If no reaction happens, there <u>won't</u> be a colour change — the halogen is <u>less reactive</u> than the halide and so can't displace it.

4) Repeat the process using different combinations of halide salt and halogen.

5) The table below shows what should happen when you mix different combinations of <u>chlorine</u>, <u>bromine</u> and <u>iodine</u> water with solutions of the salts <u>potassium chloride</u>, <u>potassium bromide</u> and <u>potassium iodide</u>.

Start with:	Potassium chloride solution $KCl_{(aq)}$ — colourless	Potassium bromide solution $KBr_{(aq)}$ — colourless	Potassium iodide solution $KI_{(aq)}$ — colourless
Add chlorine water $Cl_{2\,(aq)}$ — colourless	no reaction	orange solution (Br_2) formed	brown solution (I_2) formed
Add bromine water $Br_{2\,(aq)}$ — orange	no reaction	no reaction	brown solution (I_2) formed
Add iodine water $I_{2\,(aq)}$ — brown	no reaction	no reaction	no reaction

6) <u>Chlorine</u> displaces both bromine and iodine from salt solutions. <u>Bromine</u> can't displace chlorine, but it does displace iodine. <u>Iodine</u> can't displace chlorine or bromine.

7) This shows the <u>reactivity trend</u> — the halogens get <u>less reactive</u> as you go <u>down</u> the group.

8) You can use this trend to predict how astatine might react. Since astatine is the <u>least reactive halogen</u>, you'd predict it <u>wouldn't displace</u> any other halogens from their salt solutions.

New information displaces old information from my brain...

If you remember that the halogens get less reactive as you go down the group, you can work out what will happen when you mix any halogen with any halide salt. You need to know the colour changes that go with the reactions too.

Q1 A student added a few drops of a halogen solution to a potassium iodide solution. The solution turned brown. Explain what the student should do to help him identify the halogen solution. [2 marks]

Group 0 — Noble Gases

The elements in <u>Group 0</u> of the periodic table are known as the <u>noble gases</u>. 'Noble' here is just being used in the old chemistry sense of being <u>unreactive</u> — nothing to do with them being particularly honourable or good.

Group 0 Elements are All Inert, Colourless Gases

<u>Group 0</u> elements are called the <u>noble gases</u>. Group 0 is made up of the elements helium, neon, argon, krypton, xenon and radon.

1) All of the Group 0 elements are <u>colourless gases</u> at room temperature.

2) The noble gases are all <u>monatomic</u> — that just means that their gases are made up of <u>single atoms</u> (not molecules).

3) They're also more or less <u>inert</u> — this means they <u>don't react</u> with much at all. The reason for this is that they have a <u>full outer shell</u> of electrons. This means they <u>don't</u> easily <u>give up</u> or <u>gain</u> electrons.

4) As the noble gases are inert, they're <u>non-flammable</u> — they won't set on fire.

5) These properties make the gases pretty <u>hard to observe</u> — it took a long time for them to be discovered.

	Group 6	Group 7	Group 0
			4 He Helium 2
	O	F	20 Ne Neon 10
	S	Cl	40 Ar Argon 18
		Br	84 Kr Krypton 36
		I	131 Xe Xenon 54
		At	222 Rn Radon 86

The Noble Gases have Many Everyday Uses...

1) <u>Noble gases</u> can be used to provide an <u>inert atmosphere</u>.

2) <u>Argon</u> does this in <u>filament lamps</u> (light bulbs). Since it's <u>non-flammable</u>, it stops the very hot filament from <u>burning away</u>. <u>Flash photography</u> uses the same principle — <u>argon</u>, <u>krypton</u> and <u>xenon</u> are used to stop the flash filament from burning up during the high temperature flashes.

3) <u>Argon</u> and <u>helium</u> can also be used to protect metals that are being <u>welded</u>. The inert atmosphere stops the hot metal reacting with <u>oxygen</u>.

4) <u>Helium</u> is used in <u>airships</u> and <u>party balloons</u>. Helium has a <u>lower density</u> than air — so it makes balloons <u>float</u>. It is also <u>non-flammable</u> which makes it safer to use than hydrogen gas.

There are Patterns in the Properties of the Noble Gases

1) As with the other groups in the periodic table, there are also <u>trends</u> in the <u>properties</u> of the noble gases.

2) For example, <u>boiling point</u>, <u>melting point</u> and <u>density</u> all <u>increase</u> as you go <u>down</u> Group 0.

3) You could be given information about a particular <u>property</u> of the noble gases (or Group 7) and asked to use it to <u>estimate the value</u> of this property for a certain element. For example:

EXAMPLE: Use the densities of helium (0.2 kg m^{-3}) and argon (1.8 kg m^{-3}) to predict the density of neon.

Neon comes between helium and argon in the group, so you can predict that its density will be roughly halfway between their densities:
$(0.2 + 1.8) \div 2 = 2.0 \div 2 = 1.0$

Neon should have a density of about 1.0 kg m^{-3}.

There are other methods you could use for these types of question, but don't worry — you'd get marks for any sensible answer.

4) You could be asked about how an element <u>reacts</u> too, so remember — elements in the <u>same group</u> react in <u>similar ways</u> because they all have the same number of <u>electrons</u> in their <u>outer shells</u>. And, to find out which group an element is in, all you need to do is look at the <u>periodic table</u>. Simple.

Noble gas jokes are rubbish — I never get a reaction from them...

The noble gases might seem a bit dull, given how unreactive they are, but they're not so bad. They'd be pretty good at hide and seek for a start. And what would helium balloon sellers be without them? Deflated — that's what.

Q1 The melting points of the first four noble gases are: helium = –272 °C, neon = –249 °C, argon = –189 °C and krypton = –157 °C. Predict the melting point of xenon. [1 mark]

Reaction Rates

Reactions can be <u>fast</u> or <u>slow</u> — you've probably already realised that. It's exciting stuff. Honest.

The Rate of Reaction is a Measure of How Fast the Reaction Happens

The <u>rate of a reaction</u> is how quickly a reaction happens. It can be observed <u>either</u> by measuring how quickly the reactants are used up or how quickly the products are formed. The <u>rate of a reaction</u> can be calculated using the following formula:

$$\text{Rate of Reaction} = \frac{\text{amount of reactant used or amount of product formed}}{\text{time}}$$

It's usually a lot easier to measure products forming.

You Can Do Experiments to Follow Reaction Rates

There are different ways that the rate of a reaction can be <u>measured</u>. Here are three examples:

Precipitation

1) This method works for any reaction where mixing <u>two see-through solutions</u> produces a <u>precipitate</u>, which <u>clouds</u> the solution.

2) You <u>mix</u> the two reactant solutions and put the flask on a piece of paper that has a <u>mark</u> on it.

3) <u>Observe</u> the mark through the mixture and measure how long it takes for the mark to be <u>obscured</u>. The <u>faster</u> it disappears, the <u>faster</u> the reaction.

4) The result is <u>subjective</u> — <u>different people</u> might not agree on <u>exactly</u> when the mark 'disappears'.

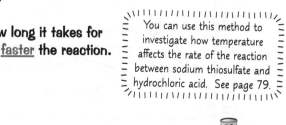

You can use this method to investigate how temperature affects the rate of the reaction between sodium thiosulfate and hydrochloric acid. See page 79.

Change in Mass (Usually Gas Given Off)

1) You can measure the rate of a reaction that <u>produces a gas</u> using a <u>mass balance</u>.

2) As the gas is released, the <u>lost mass</u> is easily measured on the balance. The <u>quicker</u> the reading on the balance <u>drops</u>, the <u>faster</u> the reaction.

3) You know the reaction has <u>finished</u> when the reading on the balance <u>stops changing</u>.

4) You can use your results to plot a <u>graph</u> of <u>change in mass</u> against <u>time</u>.

5) This method does release the gas produced straight into the room — so if the gas is <u>harmful</u>, you must take <u>safety precautions</u>, e.g. do the experiment in a <u>fume cupboard</u>.

The cotton wool lets gases through but stops any solid, liquid or aqueous reactants flying out during the reaction.

The Volume of Gas Given Off

1) This involves the use of a <u>gas syringe</u> to measure the <u>volume</u> of gas given off.

2) The <u>more</u> gas given off during a set <u>time interval</u>, the <u>faster</u> the reaction.

3) You can tell the reaction has <u>finished</u> when <u>no more gas</u> is produced.

4) You can use your results to plot a graph of <u>gas volume</u> against <u>time elapsed</u>.

5) You need to be careful that you're using the <u>right size</u> gas syringe for your experiment though — if the reaction is too <u>vigorous</u>, you can blow the plunger out of the end of the syringe.

Retraction rate — how fast my mates disappear when I tell a joke...

Lots of different ways to follow reaction rates here — well... three. Precipitation, mass loss and gas formation.

Q1   Outline how you could use a mass balance to measure the rate of a reaction where a gas is formed. [3 marks]

Q2   Give one disadvantage of the precipitation method when used to follow the rate of a reaction.   [1 mark]

PRACTICAL Rate Experiments Involving Gases

You'll probably have to <u>measure</u> the <u>rate of a reaction</u> in class at some point. Time to learn how to do it...

You can Measure how Surface Area Affects Rate

Here's how you can carry out an experiment to measure the effect of <u>surface area</u> on <u>rate</u>, using marble chips and hydrochloric acid.

1) Set the apparatus up as shown in the diagram on the right.

2) Measure the <u>volume</u> of gas produced using a <u>gas syringe</u>.
   Take readings at <u>regular time intervals</u> and record the results in a table.

3) You can plot a <u>graph</u> of your results —
   <u>time</u> goes on the <u>x-axis</u> and <u>volume</u> goes on the <u>y-axis</u>.

4) <u>Repeat</u> the experiment with <u>exactly the same volume</u> and <u>concentration</u> of acid, and <u>exactly the same mass</u> of marble chips, but with the marble <u>more crunched up</u>.

5) Then <u>repeat</u> with the same mass of <u>powdered chalk</u>.

It's important your system is air tight so no gas escapes.

CO_2 gas

dilute HCl

marble chips ($CaCO_3$)

Marble and chalk are both made of calcium carbonate ($CaCO_3$).

Finer Particles of Solid Mean a Higher Rate

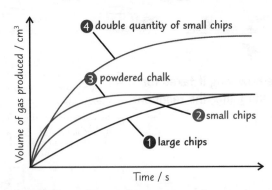

1) The <u>sooner</u> a reaction finishes, the <u>faster</u> the reaction.

2) The <u>steeper</u> the gradient of the graph, the <u>faster</u> the rate of reaction. When the line becomes flat, <u>no more gas</u> is being produced and the reaction has <u>finished</u>.

3) Using <u>finer particles</u> means that the marble has a <u>larger surface area</u>.

4) <u>Lines 1 to 3</u> on the graph on the left show that the <u>finer</u> the particles are (and the <u>greater</u> the surface area of the solid reactants), the <u>sooner</u> the reaction finishes and so the <u>faster</u> the reaction.

5) <u>Line 4</u> shows the reaction if a <u>greater mass</u> of small marble chips is added.
   The <u>extra surface area</u> gives a <u>faster reaction</u> and there is also <u>more gas evolved</u> overall.

Changing the Concentration of Acid Affects the Rate too

The reaction between marble chips and hydrochloric acid is also good for measuring how <u>changing the reactant concentration</u> affects reaction rate.

You could also measure the rate of these reactions by measuring the loss of mass as the gas is produced.

More Concentrated Solutions Mean a Higher Rate

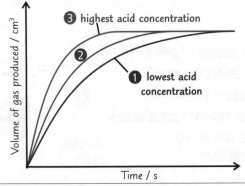

1) You can measure the effect of <u>concentration</u> on rate by following the <u>same method</u> described above. However, this time you repeat the experiment with exactly the same mass and surface area of marble chips and exactly the same volume of acid, but using <u>different concentrations</u> of acid.

2) <u>Lines 1 to 3</u> on the graph show that a <u>higher</u> concentration gives a <u>faster reaction</u>, with the reaction <u>finishing</u> sooner.

I prefer chalk to marble chips — I like the finer things in life...

Doing rate experiments lets you collect data. Collecting data lets you plot graphs, and you can use graphs to find reaction rates. But that's all still to come. I bet you're just itching to read on...

Q1   Describe how you could investigate how the surface area of calcium carbonate affects the rate of reaction between calcium carbonate and hydrochloric acid.   [3 marks]

Rate Experiments Involving Precipitation

That's right — another page, another <u>reaction rate experiment</u> to learn. But this one involves a pretty <u>precipitation</u> reaction. Beautiful stuff, don't say I don't spoil you...

Reaction Rate is Also Affected by Temperature

PRACTICAL

You can find out how temperature affects the reaction rate on page 81.

1) You can see how <u>temperature</u> affects reaction <u>rate</u> by looking at the reaction between sodium thiosulfate and hydrochloric acid.

2) Sodium thiosulfate and hydrochloric acid are both <u>clear</u>, <u>colourless solutions</u>. They react together to form a <u>yellow precipitate</u> of <u>sulfur</u>.

3) You can use the amount of <u>time</u> that it takes for the coloured precipitate to form as a measure of the <u>rate</u> of this reaction.

4) You use a method like the one on page 77 to carry out this experiment.

- Measure out fixed volumes of <u>sodium thiosulfate</u> and <u>hydrochloric acid</u>, using a measuring cylinder.
- Use a <u>water bath</u> to <u>gently heat</u> both solutions to the desired temperature before you mix them.
- Mix the solutions in a conical flask. Place the flask over a black mark on a piece of paper which can be seen through the solution. Watch the <u>black mark</u> disappear through the <u>cloudy</u>, <u>yellow sulfur</u> and <u>time</u> how long it takes to go.

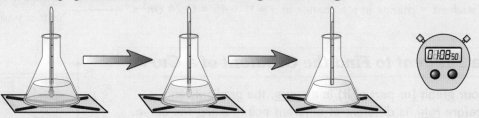

- The reaction can be repeated for solutions at <u>different temperatures</u>.
- The <u>depth</u> and <u>volumes</u> of liquid must be kept the same each time. The <u>concentrations</u> of the solutions must also be kept the same.
- You can use your results to measure what effect <u>changing the temperature</u> has on the <u>rate</u> of the reaction. The <u>shorter</u> the length of time taken for the mark to be obscured, the <u>faster</u> the rate.

Higher Temperatures Mean a Higher Rate

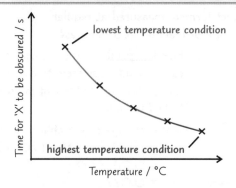

1) You can plot the <u>time taken</u> for the mark to disappear against the <u>temperature</u> of the reacting solutions.

2) If you look at the <u>graph</u>, you can see that the reactions that happened at <u>lower</u> temperatures took <u>longer</u> to obscure the mark, whereas the reactions happening at <u>higher</u> temperatures finished <u>sooner</u>.

3) So <u>increasing</u> the temperature <u>increases the rate</u> of the reaction.

How temperature, concentration and pressure affect the rate of a reaction can be explained using collision theory — see page 81.

And for my next trick, I'll make this chocolate cake disappear...

When repeating this experiment, you need to keep everything exactly the same apart from the temperature — then you can sleep easy knowing that it was the temperature change that affected the reaction rate and not anything else.

Q1 Azim carries out an experiment to measure how temperature affects the rate of reaction between sodium thiosulfate and hydrochloric acid. He uses the time taken for a mark underneath the reaction vessel to be obscured as a measure of rate. How would you expect the time taken for the mark to disappear to change as the temperature of the reacting solutions was increased?

[1 mark]

Calculating Rates

You can work out rates of reaction using graphs. I bet you can't wait to find out how...

Faster Rates of Reaction are Shown by Steeper Gradients

If you have a graph of amount of product formed (or reactant used up) against time, then the gradient (slope) of the graph will be equal to the rate of the reaction — the steeper the slope, the faster the rate.

The gradient of a straight line is given by the equation:

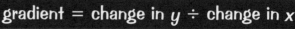

$$\text{gradient} = \text{change in } y \div \text{change in } x$$

EXAMPLE: Calculate the rate of the reaction shown on the graph on the right.

1) Find two points on the line that are easy to read the x and y values of (ones that pass through grid lines).

2) Draw a line straight down from the higher point and straight across from the lower one to make a triangle.

3) The height of your triangle = change in y
   The base of your triangle = change in x
   Change in y = 16 − 5 = 11   Change in x = 65 − 20 = 45

4) Use the formula to work out the gradient, and therefore the rate.
   Gradient = change in y ÷ change in x = 11 ÷ 45 = 0.24 cm³ s⁻¹

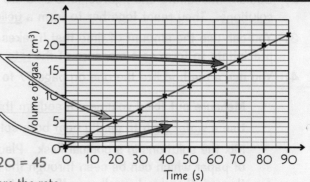

The units of the rate are just "units of y-axis ÷ units of x-axis".

Draw a Tangent to Find the Gradient of a Curve

1) If your graph (or part of it) is a curve, the gradient, and therefore rate, is different at different points along the curve.

2) To find the gradient of the graph at a certain point, you'll have to draw a tangent at that point.

3) A tangent is just a line that touches the curve and has the same gradient as the line at that point.

4) To draw a tangent, place a ruler on the line of best fit at the point you're interested in, so you can see the whole curve. Adjust the ruler so the space between the ruler and the curve is the same on both sides of the point. Draw a line along the ruler to make the tangent.

5) The rate at that point is then just the gradient of the tangent.

EXAMPLE: The graph below shows the concentration of product formed, measured at regular intervals during a chemical reaction. What is the rate of reaction at 3 minutes?

1) Position a ruler on the graph at the point where you want to know the rate — here it's 3 minutes.

2) Adjust the ruler until the space between the ruler and the curve is equal on both sides of the point.

3) Draw a line along the ruler to make the tangent. Extend the line right across the graph.

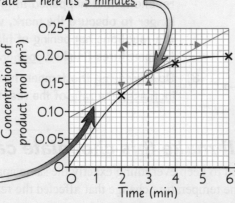

4) Pick two points on the line that are easy to read. Use them to calculate the gradient of the tangent in order to find the rate:

gradient = change in y ÷ change in x
= (0.22 − 0.14) ÷ (5.0 − 2.0)
= 0.08 ÷ 3.0
= 0.027

So, the rate of reaction at 3 minutes was 0.027 mol dm⁻³ min⁻¹.

...and that's why I love cows — oh sorry, I went off on a tangent ...

Lots of nifty graph skills here. Gradients aren't too hard, but make sure those tangents don't trip you up.

Q1   Work out the rate of reaction at 20 seconds using the graph (marked *) shown above.   [2 marks]

Collision Theory

The rate of a reaction depends on these things — <u>temperature</u>, <u>concentration</u> (or <u>pressure</u> for gases) and the <u>size of the particles</u> (for solids). This page explains why these things affect the reaction rate. Let's get cracking.

Particles Must Collide with Enough Energy in Order to React

<u>Reaction rates</u> are explained by <u>collision theory</u>. It's simple really.

The <u>rate of a chemical reaction</u> depends on:

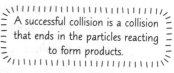
A successful collision is a collision that ends in the particles reacting to form products.

- The <u>collision frequency</u> of reacting particles (<u>how often they collide</u>). The <u>more</u> successful collisions there are, the <u>faster</u> the reaction is.
- The <u>energy transferred</u> during a collision. The minimum energy that particles need to react when they collide is called the <u>activation energy</u>. Particles need to collide with <u>at least the activation energy</u> for the collision to be <u>successful</u>.

The More Collisions, the Higher the Rate of Reaction

Reactions happen if <u>particles collide</u> with enough <u>energy</u> to react. So, if you <u>increase</u> the <u>number</u> of collisions or the <u>energy</u> with which the particles collide, the reaction happens <u>more quickly</u> (i.e. the rate increases). The three factors below all lead to an increased rate of reaction...

Increasing the Temperature Increases Rate

1) When the <u>temperature is increased</u> the particles <u>move faster</u>. If they move faster, they're going to have <u>more collisions</u>.

2) Higher temperatures also increase the <u>energy</u> of the collisions, since the particles are moving <u>faster</u>. Reactions <u>only happen</u> if the particles collide with <u>enough energy</u>.

3) This means that at <u>higher</u> temperatures there will be more <u>successful collisions</u> (<u>more particles</u> will <u>collide</u> with <u>enough energy</u> to react). So <u>increasing</u> the temperature <u>increases</u> the rate of reaction.

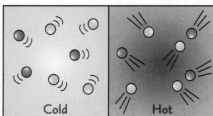
Cold   Hot

Increasing Concentration (or Pressure) Increases Rate

1) If a <u>solution</u> is made more <u>concentrated</u> it means there are more particles of <u>reactant</u> in the same volume. This makes collisions <u>more likely</u>, so the reaction rate <u>increases</u>.

2) In a <u>gas</u>, increasing the <u>pressure</u> means that the particles are <u>more crowded</u>. This means that the frequency of <u>collisions</u> between particles will <u>increase</u> — so the rate of reaction will also <u>increase</u>.

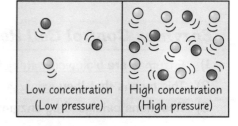
Low concentration (Low pressure)   High concentration (High pressure)

Smaller Solid Particles (or More Surface Area) Means a Higher Rate

1) If one reactant is a <u>solid</u>, breaking it into <u>smaller</u> pieces will <u>increase its surface area to volume ratio</u> (i.e. more of the solid will be exposed, compared to its overall volume).

2) The particles around it will have <u>more area to work on</u>, so the frequency of collisions will <u>increase</u>.

3) This means that the rate of reaction is faster for solids with a larger <u>surface area to volume</u> ratio.

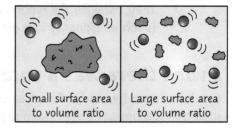
Small surface area to volume ratio   Large surface area to volume ratio

Collision theory — it's always the other driver...

Remember — more collisions mean a faster reaction. But don't be fooled as not every collision results in a reaction.

Q1   Describe the two factors, in terms of collisions, that affect the rate of reaction.   [2 marks]

Q2   Explain why breaking a solid reactant into smaller pieces increases the rate of a reaction.   [3 marks]

Catalysts

Catalysts are very important for commercial reasons — they increase reaction rate and reduce energy costs in industrial reactions. If that's not reason enough to learn this page, I don't know what is. (Oh, apart from "exams"...)

A Catalyst Increases the Rate of a Reaction

1) A catalyst is a substance which increases the rate of a reaction, without being chemically changed or used up in the reaction.

2) Using a catalyst won't change the products of the reaction — so the reaction equation will stay the same.

3) Because it isn't used up, you only need a tiny bit to catalyse large amounts of reactants.

4) Catalysts tend to be very fussy about which reactions they catalyse though — you can't just stick any old catalyst in a reaction and expect it to work.

5) Catalysts work by decreasing the activation energy (see last page) needed for a reaction to occur.

6) They do this by providing an alternative reaction pathway that has a lower activation energy.

7) As a result, more of the particles have at least the minimum amount of energy needed for a reaction to occur when the particles collide.

8) You can see this if you look at a reaction profile.

Reaction profiles show the energy levels of the reactants and the products in a reaction. There are more reaction profiles on the next page.

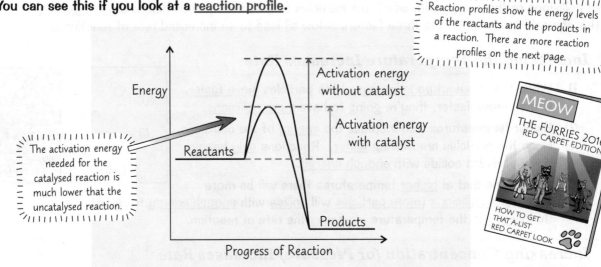

The activation energy needed for the catalysed reaction is much lower that the uncatalysed reaction.

Energy

Activation energy without catalyst

Activation energy with catalyst

Reactants

Products

Progress of Reaction

MEOW
THE FURRIES 2016
RED CARPET EDITION

HOW TO GET THAT A-LIST RED CARPET LOOK

Enzymes Control Cell Reactions

1) Enzymes are biological catalysts.

2) This means that they catalyse (speed up) the chemical reactions in living cells.

3) Reactions catalysed by enzymes include respiration, photosynthesis and protein synthesis.

- Enzymes from yeast cells are used in the fermentation process which is used to make alcoholic drinks.
- They catalyse the reaction that converts sugars (such as glucose) into ethanol and carbon dioxide.

There is more on fermentation and the production of ethanol on page 103.

I wish there was a catalyst for making my takeaway arrive...

Catalysts are really handy. Some reactions take a very long time to happen by themselves which isn't good for industrial reactions. Catalysts help to produce an acceptable amount of product in an acceptable length of time.

Q1   Give the definition of a catalyst. [2 marks]

Q2   The decomposition of hydrogen peroxide can be catalysed by manganese dioxide.
Explain why only a small amount of manganese dioxide is needed for the catalysis
of this reaction, even when starting with a large quantity of hydrogen peroxide. [1 mark]

Q3   Give the definition of an enzyme and explain what they do. [2 marks]

Endothermic and Exothermic Reactions

So, <u>endothermic</u> and <u>exothermic reactions</u> are all about taking in and giving out energy to the <u>surroundings</u>. I think endothermic reactions are a bit self centred really — they just take, take, take...

Combustion reactions (where something burns in oxygen — see page 88) are always exothermic.

Reactions are Exothermic or Endothermic

An <u>EXOTHERMIC</u> <u>reaction</u> is one which <u>gives out energy</u> to the surroundings, usually in the form of <u>heat</u> and usually shown by a <u>rise in temperature</u> of the surroundings.

An <u>ENDOTHERMIC</u> <u>reaction</u> is one which <u>takes in energy</u> from the surroundings, usually in the form of <u>heat</u> and usually shown by a <u>fall in temperature</u> of the surroundings.

Reaction Profiles Show if a Reaction's Exo- or Endothermic

<u>Reaction profiles</u> show the energy levels of the <u>reactants</u> and the <u>products</u> in a reaction. You can use them to work out if energy is <u>released</u> (exothermic) or <u>taken in</u> (endothermic).

1) This shows an <u>exothermic reaction</u> — the products are at a <u>lower energy</u> than the reactants.

2) The <u>difference in height</u> represents the <u>energy given out</u> in the reaction.

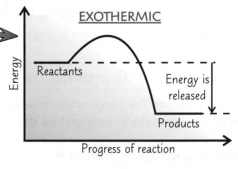

3) This shows an <u>endothermic reaction</u> because the products are at a <u>higher energy</u> than the reactants.

4) The <u>difference in height</u> represents the <u>energy taken in</u> during the reaction.

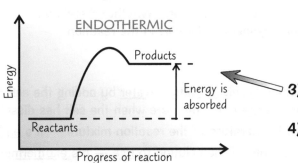

Activation Energy is the Energy Needed to Start a Reaction

1) The <u>activation energy</u> is the <u>minimum</u> amount of energy needed for <u>bonds to break</u> (see page 85) and a reaction to start.

2) On a reaction profile, it's the energy difference between the reactants and the highest point on the curve.

3) It's a bit like having to <u>climb up</u> one side of a hill before you can ski/snowboard/sledge/fall down the <u>other side</u>.

4) If the <u>energy</u> input is <u>less than</u> the activation energy there <u>won't</u> be enough energy to <u>start</u> the reaction — so nothing will happen.

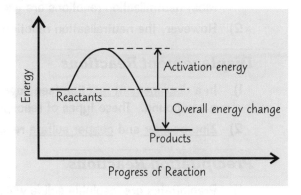

Endothermic reactions — they just get cooler and cooler...

Remember, "exo-" = exit, "-thermic" = heat, so an exothermic reaction is one that gives out heat — and endothermic means just the opposite. To make sure you really understand these terms, try this question.

Q1 A student carries out an experiment which results in a change in temperature of the reaction mixture. Use the energy profile for the reaction shown on the right to help explain whether the temperature of the reaction mixture increased or decreased.

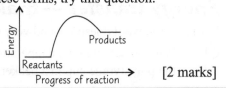

[2 marks]

Measuring Temperature Changes

Sometimes it's not enough to just know if a reaction is endothermic or exothermic. You may also need to know <u>how much</u> energy is absorbed or released — you can do experiments to find this out. Fun, fun, fun...

Temperature Changes can be Measured

You can follow the <u>change in temperature</u> of a reaction mixture as a reaction takes place. You can do this in the following way:

- Put a <u>polystyrene cup</u> into a large <u>beaker of cotton wool</u> (the cotton wool gives <u>insulation</u> to help limit energy transfer to or from the reaction mixture).
- Add a known volume of your <u>first reagent</u> to the cup.
- Measure the <u>initial temperature</u> of the solution.
- Add a measured mass/volume of your <u>second reagent</u> and <u>stir</u> the reaction mixture.
- Put a <u>lid</u> on the cup to reduce any energy lost by <u>evaporation</u>.
- Record the <u>maximum</u> or <u>minimum temperature</u> (depending on whether it's increasing or decreasing) that the mixture reaches during the reaction.
- Calculate the <u>temperature change</u>.

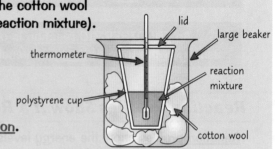

You can also use this method to see the effect that different variables have on the amount of energy transferred, e.g. the mass or concentration of the reactants.

The Change in Temperature Depends on the Reagents Used

You can measure the temperature change for <u>different types</u> of reaction. Whether there's an increase or decrease in temperature depends on which <u>reagents</u> take part in the reaction.

Dissolving Salts in Water

1) You can measure the temperature change when <u>dissolving salts in water</u> by adding the salt to a polystyrene cup of water and measuring the change in temperature when the salt has dissolved.
2) Dissolving <u>ammonium chloride decreases</u> the temperature of the reaction mixture — it's <u>endothermic</u>.
3) Dissolving <u>calcium chloride</u> causes the temperature of the solution to <u>rise</u> — it's <u>exothermic</u>.

Neutralisation Reactions

1) In a <u>neutralisation reaction</u> (see page 43), an acid and a base react to form a salt and water. Most neutralisation reactions are <u>exothermic</u>, e.g. HCl + NaOH → NaCl + H$_2$O
2) However, the neutralisation reaction between <u>ethanoic acid</u> and <u>sodium carbonate</u> is <u>endothermic</u>.

Displacement Reactions

1) In a <u>displacement reaction</u> (see page 54), a <u>more reactive</u> element <u>displaces</u> a <u>less reactive</u> element in a compound. These types of reactions are accompanied by a <u>release of energy</u> — they're <u>exothermic</u>.
2) <u>Zinc powder</u> and <u>copper sulfate</u> react in a displacement reaction forming zinc sulfate and copper.

Precipitation Reactions

1) Precipitates are insoluble solids which can sometimes form when two solutions are mixed together.
2) <u>Precipitation</u> reactions are <u>exothermic</u>. For example, the reaction between <u>lead(II) nitrate</u> solution and <u>potassium iodide</u> forming a lead iodide precipitate would result in an increase in the temperature of the surroundings.

Energy transfer — make sure you take it all in...

Fluffy cotton wool doesn't sound very sciencey but it's really important. Best check to make sure you know why...

Q1   When measuring the temperature change of a reaction, why it is important to put
      the polystyrene cup in a beaker of cotton wool and to keep a lid on the cup?   [1 mark]

Bond Energies

Energy transfer in chemical reactions is all to do with <u>making and breaking bonds</u>.

Energy Must Always be Supplied to Break Bonds

There's more on energy transfer on page 83.

1) During a chemical reaction, <u>old bonds are broken</u> and <u>new bonds are formed</u>.

2) Energy must be <u>supplied</u> to break <u>existing bonds</u> — so bond breaking is an <u>endothermic</u> process.

3) Energy is <u>released</u> when new bonds are <u>formed</u> — so bond formation is an <u>exothermic</u> process.

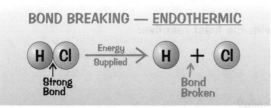

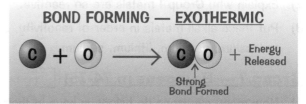

4) In <u>endothermic</u> reactions, the energy <u>used</u> to break bonds is <u>greater</u> than the energy <u>released</u> by forming them.

5) In <u>exothermic</u> reactions, the energy <u>released</u> by forming bonds is <u>greater</u> than the energy used to <u>break</u> 'em.

Bond Energy Calculations — Need to be Practised

1) <u>Every</u> chemical bond has a particular <u>bond energy</u> associated with it. This <u>bond energy</u> varies slightly depending on the <u>compound</u> the bond occurs in.

2) You can use these <u>known bond energies</u> to calculate the <u>overall energy change</u> for a reaction.

> Overall Energy Change = Energy required to break bonds − Energy released by forming bonds

3) A <u>positive</u> energy change means an <u>endothermic</u> reaction and a <u>negative</u> energy change means an <u>exothermic</u> reaction.

4) You need to <u>practise</u> a few of these, but the basic idea is really very simple...

EXAMPLE: Using the bond energy values below, calculate the energy change for the following reaction, where hydrogen and chlorine react to produce hydrogen chloride:

$$H—H + Cl—Cl \rightarrow 2H—Cl$$

H—H: 436 kJ mol⁻¹   Cl—Cl: 242 kJ mol⁻¹   H—Cl: 431 kJ mol⁻¹

1) Work out the energy required to break the <u>original bonds</u> in the reactants.

$(1 \times H—H) + (1 \times Cl—Cl) = 436 + 242$
$= 678$ kJ mol⁻¹

2) Work out the energy released by forming the <u>new bonds</u> in the products.

$(2 \times H—Cl) = 2 \times 431$
$= 862$ kJ mol⁻¹

3) Work out the overall change.

overall energy change = energy required to break bonds − energy released by forming bonds
$= 678 − 862 = −184$ kJ mol⁻¹

In this reaction, the energy released by forming bonds is greater than the energy used to break them so the reaction is exothermic.

A student and their mobile — a bond that can never be broken...

This stuff might look hard at the moment, but with a bit of practice it's dead easy and it'll win you easy marks if you understand all the theory behind it. See how you get on with this question:

Q1 During the Haber Process, N_2 reacts with H_2 in the following reaction: $N_2 + 3H_2 \rightleftharpoons 2NH_3$
The bond energies for these molecules are:
N≡N: 941 kJ mol⁻¹
H–H: 436 kJ mol⁻¹
N–H: 391 kJ mol⁻¹

Calculate the overall energy change for the forward reaction.

[3 marks]

Revision Questions for Topics 6 and 7

Would you look at that — that's another chunk of chemistry under your belt. Just a few more boxes to tick...
- Try these questions and <u>tick off each one</u> when you <u>get it right</u>.
- When you've done <u>all the questions</u> under a heading and are <u>completely happy</u> with it, tick it off.

Group 1 — Alkali Metals (p.73) ☑

1) Give two properties of the Group 1 metals. ☑
2) Explain why Group 1 metals are so reactive. ☑
3) Put these alkali metals in order of reactivity, starting with the least reactive:
potassium, caesium, lithium, sodium. ☑

Group 7 — Halogens (p.74-75) ☐

4) How many electrons do halogens have in their outer shells? ☑
5) Describe the appearances and physical states of the
following halogens at room temperature and pressure: a) chlorine,   b) bromine,   c) iodine. ☑
6) Why can halogen displacement reactions be described as redox reactions? ☑
7) If chlorine water is added to potassium bromide solution, what colour will the solution turn? ☑

Group 0 — Noble Gases (p.76) ☑

8) At room temperature, what colour are the Group 0 gases? ☑
9) Why are balloons filled with helium able to float in the air? ☑
10) Does the boiling point of Group 0 elements increase or decrease going down the group? ☑

Rates of Reaction (p.77-81) ☑

11) Explain how you could follow the rate of a reaction where
two colourless solutions react to form a precipitate. ☑
12) A student carries out a reaction which produces carbon dioxide gas. He collects the
carbon dioxide in a gas syringe. How will he know when the reaction has finished? ☑
13) Draw a diagram of the equipment you would use to measure the rate of reaction between
hydrochloric acid and marble chips. ☑
14) How does the rate of the reaction between sodium thiosulfate
and hydrochloric acid change with temperature? ☑
15) Describe how you would find the rate of a reaction from a straight line graph. ☑
16) What effect will raising the temperature have on the rate of a reaction? ☑
17) How does concentration affect the rate of a reaction? ☑
18) In a gaseous reaction, why would a decrease in pressure result in a slower rate of reaction? ☑

Catalysts (p.82) ☑

19) What effect does a catalyst have on the activation energy needed for a reaction to take place? ☑
20) Give two examples of reactions catalysed by enzymes. ☑

Energy Changes in Chemical Reactions (p.83-85) ☑

21) What change in temperature would you expect to observe in an exothermic reaction? ☑
22) What is activation energy? ☑
23) Describe how you could measure the temperature changes in a neutralisation reaction. ☑
24) Is energy required for the breaking of bonds or the forming of bonds? ☑
25) What is the equation for calculating the overall energy change for a reaction? ☑

Fractional Distillation

Fossil fuels like coal, oil and gas are called non-renewable fuels — they take so long to make that they're being used up much faster than they're being formed. They're finite resources — one day they'll run out.

Crude Oil is Separated into Different Hydrocarbon Fractions

1) Crude oil is our main source of hydrocarbons and is used as a raw material (sometimes called a feedstock) to create lots of useful substances used in the petrochemical industry.

2) It's formed underground, over millions of years (at high temperatures and pressures) from the buried remains of plants and animals. It's a non-renewable (finite) resource, so one day it will run out.

3) Crude oil is a complex mixture of lots of different hydrocarbons — compounds which contain just carbon and hydrogen. The hydrocarbons found in crude oil have their carbon atoms arranged in either chains or rings and are mostly alkanes (hydrocarbons with the general formula C_nH_{2n+2}).

4) Crude oil can be separated out into fractions — simpler, more useful mixtures containing groups of hydrocarbons of similar lengths (i.e. they have similar numbers of carbon and hydrogen atoms). The fractions from crude oil, e.g. petrol, kerosene and diesel, are examples of non-renewable fossil fuels. Methane, the main component of natural gas, is another non-renewable fossil fuel. ⬅ Natural gas is a mixture of gases which forms underground in a similar way to crude oil.

5) The different fractions in crude oil are separated by fractional distillation. The oil is heated until most of it has turned into gas. The gases enter a fractionating column (and the liquid bit, bitumen, is drained off at the bottom).

6) In the column there's a temperature gradient (i.e. it's hot at the bottom and gets cooler as you go up).

7) The longer hydrocarbons have higher boiling points. They turn back into liquids and drain out of the column early on, when they're near the bottom. The shorter hydrocarbons have lower boiling points. They turn to liquid and drain out much later on, near to the top of the column where it's cooler.

8) You end up with the crude oil mixture separated out into different fractions. Each fraction contains a mixture of hydrocarbons, mostly alkanes (see page 98) with similar boiling points.

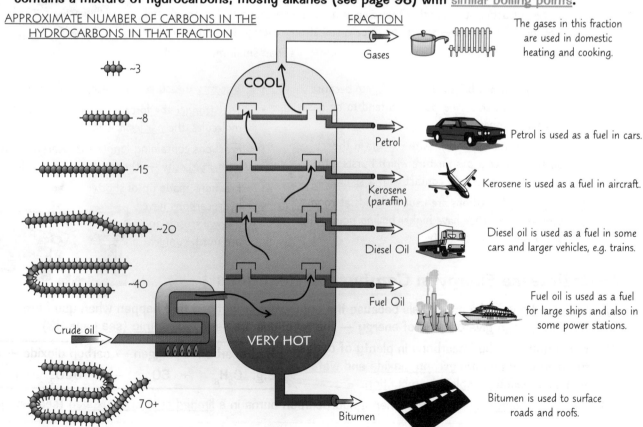

APPROXIMATE NUMBER OF CARBONS IN THE HYDROCARBONS IN THAT FRACTION

FRACTION

~3

~8

~15

~20

~40

Crude oil

70+

COOL

VERY HOT

Gases — The gases in this fraction are used in domestic heating and cooking.

Petrol — Petrol is used as a fuel in cars.

Kerosene (paraffin) — Kerosene is used as a fuel in aircraft.

Diesel Oil — Diesel oil is used as a fuel in some cars and larger vehicles, e.g. trains.

Fuel Oil — Fuel oil is used as a fuel for large ships and also in some power stations.

Bitumen — Bitumen is used to surface roads and roofs.

How much petrol is there in crude oil? Just a fraction...

Crude oil is pretty useful, so it's worth having a good read of this page to make sure you know all about it.

Q1   Explain how crude oil is separated into fractions during fractional distillation.   [5 marks]

Hydrocarbons

The <u>physical properties</u> of crude oil fractions all depend on how <u>big</u> the hydrocarbons in that fraction are.

Compounds in a Homologous Series Share Similar Chemical Properties

1) A <u>homologous series</u> is a <u>family</u> of molecules which have the same <u>general formula</u> and share similar <u>chemical properties</u>.

2) The molecular formulas of <u>neighbouring compounds</u> in a homologous series differ by a <u>CH$_2$</u> unit.

3) The physical properties of compounds in a homologous series vary between the different molecules. For example, the <u>bigger</u> a molecule is, the <u>higher</u> the <u>boiling point</u> will be (see below).

Alkane	Molecular formula	Boiling point (°C)	Fraction in crude oil
Methane	CH_4	−162	Gases
Ethane	C_2H_6	−89	Gases
Dodecane	$C_{12}H_{26}$	216	Kerosene
Icosane	$C_{20}H_{42}$	343	Diesel Oil
Tetracontane	$C_{40}H_{82}$	524	Fuel Oil

4) <u>Alkanes</u> and <u>alkenes</u> (see page 98) are two different homologous series of hydrocarbons.

The Size of a Hydrocarbon Determines its Properties

1) The <u>size</u> of a hydrocarbon determines which <u>fraction</u> of crude oil it will separate into (see last page).

2) Each fraction contains hydrocarbons (mostly <u>alkanes</u>) with <u>similar</u> numbers of <u>carbon</u> atoms, so all of the molecules in a fraction will have <u>similar properties</u> and behave in similar ways.

3) The <u>physical properties</u> are determined by the <u>intermolecular forces</u> that hold the chains together.

- The <u>intermolecular forces</u> of attraction break a lot more <u>easily</u> in <u>small</u> molecules than they do in bigger molecules. That's because the forces are much <u>stronger</u> between big molecules than they are between small molecules.

- It makes sense if you think about it — even if a big molecule can overcome the forces attracting it to another molecule at a <u>few points</u> along its length, it's still got lots of <u>other</u> places where the force is still strong enough to hold it in place.

- That's why <u>big</u> molecules have <u>higher boiling points</u> than small molecules do.

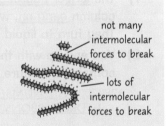

not many intermolecular forces to break

lots of intermolecular forces to break

- <u>Shorter</u> hydrocarbons are <u>easy to ignite</u> because they have lower boiling points, so tend to be gases at room temperature.

- These gas molecules mix with <u>oxygen</u> in the air to produce a gas mixture which bursts into flames if it comes into contact with a <u>spark</u>.

- <u>Longer</u> hydrocarbons are usually <u>liquids</u> at room temperature. They have higher boiling points and are much <u>harder</u> to ignite.

- <u>Viscosity</u> measures how easily a substance <u>flows</u>.

- The <u>stronger</u> the force is between hydrocarbon molecules, the <u>harder</u> it is for the liquid to <u>flow</u>.

- Fractions containing <u>longer</u> hydrocarbons have a <u>higher viscosity</u> — they're <u>thick</u> like treacle.

- Fractions made up of <u>shorter</u> hydrocarbons have a <u>low viscosity</u> and are much <u>runnier</u>.

Premium Grade Treacle

Fuels Release Energy in Combustion Reactions

1) <u>Hydrocarbons</u> make great fuels because the <u>combustion reactions</u> that happen when you burn them in <u>oxygen</u> give out lots of energy — the reactions are very <u>exothermic</u> (see page 83).

2) When you burn hydrocarbons in plenty of oxygen, the only products are <u>carbon dioxide</u> and <u>water</u> — this is called <u>complete combustion</u>.

> Hydrocarbon + oxygen → carbon dioxide + water
> E.g. C_3H_8 + $5O_2$ → $3CO_2$ + $4H_2O$

3) <u>Incomplete combustion</u> occurs when a hydrocarbon burns in a <u>limited supply of oxygen</u> (see next page).

My sister has a high viscosity — she's pretty thick...

So, the difference in properties is all down to the intermolecular forces between the hydrocarbon chains. For long hydrocarbons, just remember the three H's — <u>h</u>igher boiling points, <u>h</u>igher viscosity and <u>h</u>arder to ignite.

Q1   Write a balanced symbol equation to show the complete combustion of C_9H_{20} (nonane).   [2 marks]

Pollutants

You get loads of nasties like carbon monoxide, oxides of nitrogen and sulfur dioxide when you burn fossil fuels.

Incomplete Combustion Produces Toxic Carbon Monoxide and Soot

1) Complete combustion reactions of hydrocarbons produce only carbon dioxide and water (see last page).

2) If there's not enough oxygen around for complete combustion, you get incomplete combustion. This can happen in some appliances, e.g. boilers, that use carbon compounds as fuels.

3) The products of incomplete combustion contain less oxygen than carbon dioxide.

4) As well as carbon dioxide and water, incomplete combustion produces carbon monoxide (CO), a toxic gas, and carbon in the form of soot.

In reality, incomplete combustion reactions will usually produce a mixture of H_2O, CO_2, CO and C.

- Carbon monoxide can combine with red blood cells and stop your blood from doing its proper job of carrying oxygen around the body.
- A lack of oxygen in the blood supply to the brain can lead to fainting, a coma or even death.

- During incomplete combustion, tiny particles of carbon can be released into the atmosphere. When they fall back to the ground, they deposit themselves as the horrible black dust we call soot.
- Soot makes buildings look dirty, reduces air quality and can cause or worsen respiratory problems.

Sulfur Dioxide Causes Acid Rain

1) When fossil fuels are burned, they release mostly CO_2 (a big cause of global warming, see page 93).

2) But they also release other harmful gases — especially sulfur dioxide and various nitrogen oxides.

3) The sulfur dioxide (SO_2) comes from sulfur impurities in the fossil fuels.

4) When sulfur dioxide mixes with clouds, it forms dilute sulfuric acid. This then falls as acid rain.

5) Acid rain causes lakes to become acidic and many plants and animals die as a result.

6) Acid rain kills trees, damages limestone buildings and stone statues and can also make metal corrode.

Oxides of Nitrogen Are Also Pollutants

1) Nitrogen oxides are created from a reaction between the nitrogen and oxygen in the air, caused by the energy released by combustion reactions, for example, in the internal combustion engines of cars.

2) Nitrogen oxides are harmful pollutants — they can contribute to acid rain and, at ground level, can cause photochemical smog.

3) Photochemical smog is a type of air pollution that can cause breathing difficulties, headaches and tiredness.

Hydrogen can be Used as a Clean, Renewable Fuel

Hydrogen gas can also be used to power vehicles. It's often used as a fuel in fuel cells (see page 71).

Pros: Hydrogen is a very clean fuel. In a hydrogen fuel cell, hydrogen combines with oxygen to produce energy, and the only waste product is water — no nasty pollutants like carbon dioxide, toxic carbon monoxide or soot (which are produced when fossil fuels are burnt). Hydrogen's obtained from water which is a renewable resource, so it's not going to run out (unlike fossil fuels). Hydrogen can even be obtained from the water produced by the cell when it's used in fuel cells.

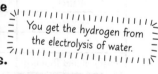
You get the hydrogen from the electrolysis of water.

Cons: You need a special, expensive engine. Hydrogen gas also needs to be manufactured which is expensive and often uses energy from another source — this energy often comes from burning fossil fuels which produces pollutants. Also, hydrogen's hard to store and not widely available.

Do you want to hear a joke about nitrogen monoxide? NO?

Acid rain's bad news for sculptors, fish and trees alike. It's bad news for you too, as you need to know it...

Q1   Name two pollutants formed by incomplete combustion.   [2 marks]

Cracking

Crude oil fractions from fractional distillation are split into <u>smaller molecules</u> — this is called <u>cracking</u>. It's dead important — otherwise we might not have enough fuel for cars and planes and things.

Cracking is Splitting Up Long-Chain Hydrocarbons

1) <u>Cracking</u> turns long saturated (alkane) molecules into <u>smaller unsaturated</u> (<u>alkene</u>) and <u>alkane</u> molecules (which are much more <u>useful</u>).

2) It's a form of <u>thermal decomposition</u>, which is when one substance <u>breaks down</u> into at least two new ones when you <u>heat it</u>. This means breaking <u>strong covalent bonds</u>, so you need <u>lots of energy</u>. A <u>catalyst</u> is often added to speed things up.

3) A lot of the longer molecules produced from <u>fractional distillation</u> are <u>cracked</u> into smaller ones because there's <u>more demand</u> for products like <u>petrol</u> and <u>diesel</u> than for bitumen and fuel oil.

4) Cracking also produces lots of <u>alkene</u> molecules, which can be used to make <u>polymers</u> (mostly plastics).

Cracking Involves Heat, Moderate Pressures and a Catalyst

1) <u>Vaporised hydrocarbons</u> are passed over <u>powdered catalyst</u> at about <u>400 °C – 700 °C</u> and <u>70 atm</u>.

2) <u>Aluminium oxide</u> is the <u>catalyst</u> used. The <u>long-chain</u> molecules <u>split apart</u> or "crack" on the <u>surface</u> of the bits of catalyst.

You don't need to remember the conditions used for cracking.

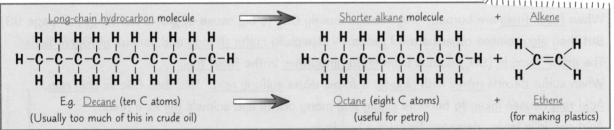

E.g. <u>Decane</u> (ten C atoms) (Usually too much of this in crude oil) → <u>Octane</u> (eight C atoms) (useful for petrol) + <u>Ethene</u> (for making plastics)

3) You can use the apparatus shown below to crack <u>alkanes</u> in the lab. During this reaction, the alkane is heated until it is <u>vaporised</u>. It then breaks down when it comes into contact with the catalyst, producing a mixture of <u>short-chain alkanes</u> and <u>alkenes</u>.

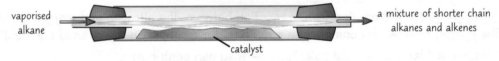

vaporised alkane — catalyst — a mixture of shorter chain alkanes and alkenes

Cracking Helps Match Supply and Demand

The examiner might give you a <u>table</u> like the one below to show the <u>supply</u> and <u>demand</u> for various fractions obtained from crude oil. You could be asked which fraction is <u>more likely to be cracked</u> to provide us with petrol and diesel oil (demand for petrol and diesel oil is greater than the amount in crude oil).

Fraction	Approx % in crude oil	Approx % demand
Gases	2	4
Petrol	16	27
Kerosene	13	8
Diesel Oil	19	23
Fuel Oil and Bitumen	50	38

OK, you could use the <u>kerosene fraction</u> to supply the extra <u>petrol</u> and the <u>fuel oil and bitumen fraction</u> to supply the extra <u>diesel oil</u>.

Or you could crack the <u>fuel oil and bitumen</u> to supply <u>both</u> the extra <u>petrol</u> and the extra <u>diesel oil</u>. This might be cleverer, as there's a lot more fuel oil/bitumen than kerosene.

Aluminium oxide's hilarious, it's always cracking the alkanes up...

In that case, I better crack open another packet of biscuits so that the supply matches my stomach's large demand...

Q1 Why does the process of cracking require lots of energy? [1 mark]

Q2 When a molecule of $C_{17}H_{36}$ is cracked under certain conditions, two molecules are made. If one of the product molecules is C_5H_{10}, what is the chemical formula of the other product? [1 mark]

The Atmosphere

Scientists have looked at <u>evidence</u> from rocks, air bubbles in ice and fossils to see how our <u>atmosphere</u> has <u>changed</u> over many, many years. Here's one theory about how our atmosphere might have evolved.

Phase 1 — Volcanoes Gave Out Steam and CO₂

The First Billion Years

<u>Holiday report</u>: Not nice. Take strong walking boots and a coat.

1) The Earth's surface was originally <u>molten</u> for many millions of years. There was almost no atmosphere.

2) Eventually the Earth's surface cooled and a <u>thin crust</u> formed, but <u>volcanoes</u> kept erupting, releasing gases from <u>inside the Earth</u>. This 'degassing' released mainly <u>carbon dioxide</u>, but also <u>steam</u>, <u>methane</u> and <u>ammonia</u>.

3) When things eventually settled down, the early atmosphere was <u>mostly CO₂</u> and water vapour. There was very little oxygen.

4) The water vapour later <u>condensed</u> to form the <u>oceans</u>.

Phase 2 — Green Plants Evolved and Produced Oxygen

The Next Two Billion Years

<u>Holiday Report</u>: A bit slimy underfoot. Take wellies and a lot of suncream.

1) A lot of the early CO₂ <u>dissolved</u> into the oceans.

2) <u>Nitrogen gas</u> (<u>N₂</u>) was then put into the atmosphere in two ways — it was formed by ammonia reacting with oxygen, and was released by denitrifying bacteria.

3) <u>N₂</u> isn't very <u>reactive</u>. So the amount of N₂ in the atmosphere <u>increased</u>, because it was being <u>made</u> but not <u>broken down</u>.

4) Next, <u>green plants</u> evolved over most of the Earth. As they photosynthesised, they <u>removed CO₂</u> and <u>produced O₂</u>.

5) Thanks to the plants, the amount of O₂ in the air gradually <u>built up</u> and much of the CO₂ eventually got <u>locked up</u> in <u>fossil fuels</u> and <u>sedimentary rocks</u>.

Phase 3 — Ozone Layer Allows Evolution of Complex Animals

The Last Billion Years or so

OZONE layer, O₃

<u>Holiday report</u>: A nice place to be. Get there before the crowds ruin it.

1) The build-up of <u>oxygen</u> in the atmosphere <u>killed off</u> early organisms that couldn't tolerate it.

2) But it did allow the <u>evolution</u> of more <u>complex</u> organisms that <u>made use</u> of the oxygen.

3) The oxygen also created the <u>ozone layer</u> (O₃), which <u>blocked</u> harmful rays from the Sun and <u>enabled</u> even <u>more complex</u> organisms to evolve.

4) There is virtually <u>no CO₂</u> left now.

<u>Today's atmosphere</u> is made up of:
- approximately <u>78% nitrogen</u> and approximately <u>21% oxygen</u>,
- small amounts of other gases (each making up <u>less than 1%</u> of the atmosphere), mainly carbon dioxide, noble gases and water vapour.

Test for Oxygen Using a Glowing Splint

You can <u>test</u> for oxygen by checking if the gas will <u>relight</u> a <u>glowing splint</u>.

glowing splint

I went to a restaurant on the moon — nice view, no atmosphere...

We can breathe easy knowing that our atmosphere has developed into a lovely oxygen rich one. Aaaahh.

Q1 The atmosphere of Earth was originally composed mostly of carbon dioxide.
Explain how the proportion of carbon dioxide in the atmosphere decreased over time. [3 marks]

The Greenhouse Effect

The <u>greenhouse effect</u> isn't a bumper crop of tomatoes and a prize winning marrow...

Human Activity Affects the Composition of Air

1) Over the last 150 years or so, the <u>human population has increased rapidly</u>.

2) More people means that <u>more energy</u> is needed for lighting, heating, cooking, transport and so on. People's <u>lifestyles</u> are changing too. More and more countries are becoming <u>industrialised</u> and <u>well-off</u>. This means the average <u>energy demand per person</u> is also increasing (since people have <u>more electrical gadgets</u>, more people have <u>cars</u> or <u>travel on planes</u>, etc.). This increased energy consumption comes mainly from the <u>burning of fossil fuels</u>, which releases <u>more CO_2</u>.

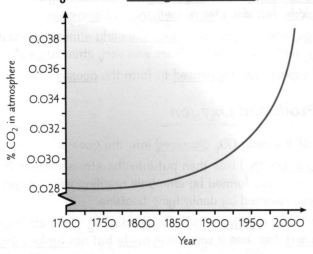

So, as the consumption of fossil fuels increases, as does the concentration of CO_2 in the atmosphere.

3) More people also means more land is needed to build <u>houses</u> and grow <u>food</u>. This space is often made by <u>chopping down trees</u> — this is called <u>deforestation</u>. But plants are the main things <u>taking carbon dioxide out of the atmosphere</u> (as they photosynthesise) — so fewer plants means less carbon dioxide is <u>taken out</u> of the atmosphere.

4) CO_2 is also produced by <u>volcanoes erupting</u>.

5) The graph shows how CO_2 levels in the atmosphere have <u>risen</u> over the last 300 years.

The Greenhouse Effect Helps to Keep the Earth Warm

The greenhouse effect is very important — it's what keeps the Earth warm enough for us to live on.

1) The <u>Sun</u> gives out <u>electromagnetic radiation</u>.

2) <u>Some</u> electromagnetic radiation, at most wavelengths, <u>passes through</u> the atmosphere.

3) The electromagnetic radiation with short wavelengths is <u>absorbed</u> by the Earth — <u>warming</u> our planet.

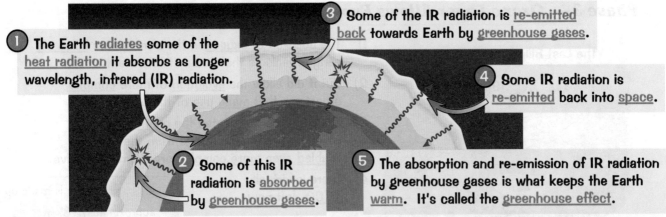

1 The Earth <u>radiates</u> some of the <u>heat radiation</u> it absorbs as longer wavelength, infrared (IR) radiation.

2 Some of this IR radiation is <u>absorbed</u> by <u>greenhouse gases</u>.

3 Some of the IR radiation is <u>re-emitted back</u> towards Earth by <u>greenhouse gases</u>.

4 Some IR radiation is <u>re-emitted</u> back into <u>space</u>.

5 The absorption and re-emission of IR radiation by greenhouse gases is what keeps the Earth <u>warm</u>. It's called the <u>greenhouse effect</u>.

<u>Greenhouse gases</u> are the <u>gases</u> in the atmosphere that can <u>absorb and reflect heat radiation</u>. They're only present in <u>small amounts</u>. <u>Carbon dioxide</u>, <u>water vapour</u> and <u>methane</u> are three <u>greenhouse gases</u>.

4) If the concentration of greenhouse gases in the atmosphere increases, you get an <u>enhanced greenhouse effect</u>. This is where <u>more heat radiation</u> from the Earth is absorbed and less is re-emitted back into space. This causes the atmosphere to <u>heat up</u> (see next page).

The White House effect — heated political debates...

Is all this hot air isn't making you a bit hot and bothered? If so, here are some questions to cheer you up.

Q1   Give the definition of a greenhouse gas.   [1 mark]

Q2   Give two reasons why the increasing human population has affected levels of atmospheric CO_2. [2 marks]

Climate Change

Is it me, or is it getting <u>hot</u> in here...?

Increasing Greenhouse Gases Causes Climate Change

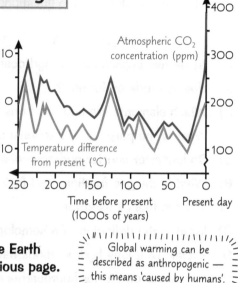

1) You saw on the last page that the level of <u>carbon dioxide</u> in the atmosphere is <u>increasing</u>, but that's not the whole story...

2) The greenhouse gas methane is also causing problems. The concentration of <u>methane</u> has risen lots in recent years due to increased human activity. Methane is produced in the <u>digestive processes</u> of certain <u>livestock</u> (e.g. cattle, goats and camels). So, the more livestock we farm, the more methane is produced.

3) Though it's currently only present in <u>tiny amounts</u> in our atmosphere, the increasing concentration of methane is an issue as it's a super effective <u>greenhouse gas</u>.

4) There's a <u>scientific consensus</u> that extra greenhouse gases from <u>human activity</u> have caused the average <u>temperature</u> of the Earth to <u>increase</u>, due to the enhanced greenhouse effect — see previous page. This effect is known as global warming.

Global warming can be described as anthropogenic — this means 'caused by humans'.

5) Global warming is a type of <u>climate change</u> and causes other types of climate change, e.g. changing rainfall patterns. It could also cause severe <u>flooding</u> due to the polar ice caps melting. It's a BIG problem that could affect the whole world, so we need to deal with it seriously.

Historical Data is Much Less Accurate Than Current Records

1) <u>Current global temperature</u> and <u>carbon dioxide levels</u> can be worked out pretty accurately as they're based on measurements taken all over the world.

2) Historical data is <u>less accurate</u> — less data was taken over fewer locations and the methods used to collect the data were less accurate. If you go back far enough, there are <u>no records</u> of global temperature and carbon dioxide levels at all...

3) But there are ways to <u>estimate past data</u>. For example, you can analyse <u>fossils</u>, <u>tree rings</u> or <u>gas bubbles</u> trapped in <u>ice sheets</u> to estimate past levels of atmospheric carbon dioxide.

4) The problem with using these kinds of measurements is that they're much <u>less precise</u> than current measurements made using <u>instrumental sampling</u>. They're also much <u>less representative</u> of global levels.

We Can Try To Use Less Fossil Fuels

Aaaaaah! The gases have escaped!!

1) In order to prevent or <u>slow down climate change</u>, we need to <u>cut down</u> on the amount of greenhouse gases we're releasing into the atmosphere.

2) To <u>reduce carbon dioxide emissions</u>, we can try to limit our own use of fossil fuels. This could be doing things on a personal level, like <u>walking</u> or <u>cycling</u> instead of driving or <u>turning your central heating down</u>.

3) On a larger scale, the UK government has formed plans to encourage the public and industry to become more <u>energy efficient</u>, to create financial incentives to reduce CO_2 emissions, to use more renewable energy and to increase research into new energy sources.

Give the climate some privacy — it's changing...

It's not all depressing news. There are steps we can take to cut our carbon dioxide emissions, so chin up.

Q1   What is global warming and how is it caused?   [2 marks]

Q2   Give two measures we can take to reduce carbon dioxide emissions.   [2 marks]

Revision Questions for Topic 8

That's <u>Topic 8</u> down, which means there's only one more topic standing between you end the end. Yay.
- Try these questions and <u>tick off each one</u> when you <u>get it right</u>.
- When you've done <u>all the questions</u> under a heading and are <u>completely happy</u> with it, tick it off.

<u>Fractional Distillation of Crude Oil and Fuels (p.87-88)</u> ☑

1) Name two applications of hydrocarbons. ☑
2) How is crude oil formed? ☑
3) Which elements are hydrocarbons made from? ☑
4) What is the purpose of fractional distillation? ☑
5) Do longer or shorter hydrocarbons drain out near the bottom of the fractional distillation column? ☑
6) What is the gas fraction used for? ☑
7) What is fuel oil used for? ☑
8) What is the definition of a homologous series? ☑
9) Explain why long hydrocarbons have a high boiling point. ☑
10) Are longer or shorter hydrocarbons associated with a low viscosity? ☑
11) Give the word equation for the complete combustion of hydrocarbons. ☑

<u>Pollutants (p.89)</u> ☑

12) Why does incomplete combustion occur? ☑
13) Why is carbon monoxide bad for human health? ☑
14) Name a gas that contributes to the production of acid rain. ☑
15) Give three problems associated with acid rain. ☑

<u>Cracking (p.90)</u> ☑

16) What is cracking? ☑
17) What types of molecules are produced by cracking? ☑

<u>The Atmosphere (p.91)</u> ☑

18) Name the gases given out by volcanoes millions of years ago. ☑
19) How was nitrogen gas originally put into the atmosphere? ☑
20) What change in the early atmosphere allowed the complex organisms to evolve? ☑
21) How could you test an unknown gas to see if it was oxygen? ☑

<u>The Greenhouse Effect and Climate Change (p.92-93)</u> ☑

22) Outline how the greenhouse effect works. ☑
23) How has human activity led to an increase in the concentration of methane in the atmosphere? ☑
24) What methods have scientists used to predict past climates? ☑

Tests for Cations

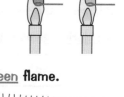

PRACTICAL

So, <u>tests</u> for <u>identifying cations</u> in mystery compounds probably don't get your heart racing with excitement, but this section includes lots of different <u>colours</u> so just think of all the pretty revision notes you could make...

You Can Use Flame Tests to Identify Metal Ions

<u>Compounds</u> of some <u>metals</u> produce a <u>characteristic colour</u> when heated in a <u>flame</u>.

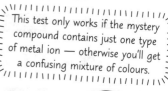

Li+   Cu²⁺

1) You can test for various <u>metal ions</u> by putting your substance in a <u>flame</u> and seeing what <u>colour</u> the flame goes.

   <u>Lithium</u> ions, Li^+, give a (crimson) <u>red</u> flame.   <u>Calcium</u> ions, Ca^{2+},
   <u>Sodium</u> ions, Na^+, give a <u>yellow</u> flame.   give an <u>orange-red</u> flame.
   <u>Potassium</u> ions, K^+, give a <u>lilac</u> flame.   <u>Copper</u> ions, Cu^{2+}, give a <u>blue-green</u> flame.

2) To carry out a flame test in the lab, first <u>clean</u> a <u>nichrome wire loop</u> by dipping it into <u>hydrochloric acid</u> and then rinsing it in <u>distilled water</u>.

This test only works if the mystery compound contains just one type of metal ion — otherwise you'll get a confusing mixture of colours.

3) Then dip the <u>wire loop</u> into a sample of the <u>metal compound</u> and put the loop in the clear blue part of a Bunsen flame (the hottest bit). Record what <u>colour</u> the flame goes.

Some Metal Ions Form a Coloured Precipitate with NaOH

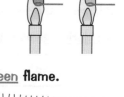

SILENCE COPPER TEST IN PROGRESS

This is also a test for metal ions, but it's slightly more complicated:

1) Many <u>metal hydroxides</u> are <u>insoluble</u> and precipitate out of solution when formed. Some of these hydroxides have a <u>characteristic colour</u>.

2) For this test, you add a few drops of <u>sodium hydroxide solution</u> to a solution of your mystery compound.

3) If a <u>hydroxide precipitate</u> forms, you can use its <u>colour</u> to tell which metal ion was in the compound.

Metal ion	Colour of precipitate	Ionic equation
Aluminium, Al^{3+}	**White** at first, but then redissolves in excess NaOH to form a **colourless** solution.	$Al^{3+}_{(aq)} + 3OH^-_{(aq)} \rightarrow Al(OH)_{3(s)}$ Then: $Al(OH)_{3(s)} + OH^-_{(aq)} \rightarrow Al(OH)_4^-_{(aq)}$
Calcium, Ca^{2+}	**White**	$Ca^{2+}_{(aq)} + 2OH^-_{(aq)} \rightarrow Ca(OH)_{2(s)}$
Copper, Cu^{2+}	Blue	$Cu^{2+}_{(aq)} + 2OH^-_{(aq)} \rightarrow Cu(OH)_{2(s)}$
Iron(II), Fe^{2+}	Green	$Fe^{2+}_{(aq)} + 2OH^-_{(aq)} \rightarrow Fe(OH)_{2(s)}$
Iron(III), Fe^{3+}	Brown	$Fe^{3+}_{(aq)} + 3OH^-_{(aq)} \rightarrow Fe(OH)_{3(s)}$

There's more about ionic equations on page 13.

Adding NaOH to Ammonium Ions Produces Ammonia

1) To work out whether a substance contains <u>ammonium ions</u> (NH_4^+), all you need to do is add some <u>sodium hydroxide</u> solution to a solution of your mystery substance and gently heat it. If ammonia gas is given off, it means that there are ammonium ions in your mystery substance.

2) You can test for <u>ammonia gas</u> by holding a piece of <u>damp red litmus paper</u> over it. If the mystery gas is ammonia, the litmus paper will <u>turn blue</u>.

3) Ammonia also has a very distinctive <u>strong smell</u>, but it's not a good idea to go sniffing a mystery gas to figure out what it is — for example, at high concentrations, ammonia is an <u>irritant</u> and <u>toxic</u>.

ammonia

damp red litmus paper

Cations — ions with a pawsitive charge...

Lots of ions and colours to learn here, so just take your time. I like to remember Li⁺ttle Red Riding Hood.

Q1   A compound is heated in a flame. A lilac flame is produced. What does this show?   [1 mark]

Q2   A few drops of sodium hydroxide are added to an unknown solution.
      A brown precipitate forms. What does this tell you about the solution?   [1 mark]

PRACTICAL

Tests for Anions

I hope you've got your special detective hat on because we have another page on <u>identifying ions</u> in mystery compounds. Now we're testing for <u>negative ions</u>, but try to keep positive, it's really not that bad...

Test for Halide Ions Using Silver Nitrate Solution

To test for <u>chloride</u> ions (Cl⁻), <u>bromide</u> ions (Br⁻) or <u>iodide</u> ions (I⁻), add some <u>dilute nitric acid</u> (HNO₃), followed by a few drops of <u>silver nitrate solution</u> (AgNO₃).

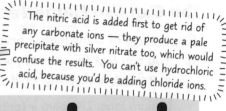

The nitric acid is added first to get rid of any carbonate ions — they produce a pale precipitate with silver nitrate too, which would confuse the results. You can't use hydrochloric acid, because you'd be adding chloride ions.

A <u>chloride</u> gives a white precipitate of <u>silver chloride</u>.

$$Ag^+_{(aq)} + Cl^-_{(aq)} \longrightarrow AgCl_{(s)}$$

A <u>bromide</u> gives a cream precipitate of <u>silver bromide</u>.

$$Ag^+_{(aq)} + Br^-_{(aq)} \longrightarrow AgBr_{(s)}$$

An <u>iodide</u> gives a yellow precipitate of <u>silver iodide</u>.

$$Ag^+_{(aq)} + I^-_{(aq)} \longrightarrow AgI_{(s)}$$

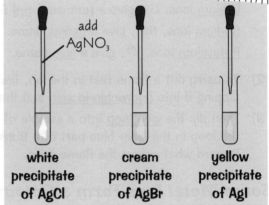

add AgNO₃

white precipitate of AgCl   cream precipitate of AgBr   yellow precipitate of AgI

Test for Carbonates Using Dilute Acid

1) To test for <u>carbonate ions</u> (CO₃²⁻) in solution, add some dilute <u>acid</u>.

2) If there are carbonate ions present, the mixture will <u>fizz</u> — this is because the carbonate will react with the acid to produce <u>carbon dioxide gas</u>:

carbonate ions + acid → carbon dioxide + water
$$CO_3^{2-} + 2H^+ \rightarrow CO_2 + H_2O$$

The test for carbon dioxide is covered on page 45.

3) You can check to see if a gas is <u>carbon dioxide</u> by bubbling it through <u>limewater</u>. If it is carbon dioxide, the limewater turns <u>milky</u>.

Test for Sulfate Ions Using Barium Chloride Solution

1) To test for <u>sulfate ions</u> in solution, first add some <u>dilute hydrochloric acid</u> to the test sample — this stops any precipitation reactions not involving sulfate ions from taking place.

2) Then add some <u>barium chloride solution</u>. If there are sulfate ions in the solution, a <u>white precipitate</u> of barium sulfate will form:

barium ions + sulfate ions → barium sulfate
$$Ba^{2+}_{(aq)} + SO_4^{2-}_{(aq)} \rightarrow BaSO_{4(s)}$$

Anne irons.

The Test for Each Ion must be Unique

1) It's important that you know the <u>tests</u> for all the <u>ions</u> on this page, and the last page for that matter.

2) Each test is <u>unique</u> — it gives certain results depending on the ions present. It would be no good if each test gave the <u>same response</u> for <u>different ions</u> — that way you'd have <u>no idea</u> of knowing what ions you actually had in a given sample.

Chop them and see if you cry — oh wait, you said test for anions...

Unfortunately, the colours here aren't quite as exciting as those in tests for cations but they are just as important...

Q1   A chemist adds some dilute nitric acid to a solution, X, followed by some silver nitrate solution. A yellow precipitate forms. What does this tell the chemist about solution X?   [1 mark]

Flame Photometry

Flame photometry is a pretty groovy technique that can <u>accurately identify</u> different metal ions in solution and find their <u>concentrations</u>. And as a bonus, it produces some more lovely colours. What more could you want?

Every Metal Ion Gives a Characteristic Line Spectrum

1) Flame photometry is an <u>instrumental method</u> that allows you to <u>identify</u> ions in a dilute solution.

2) Each ion produces a unique <u>line spectrum</u> with different lines present in different places.

3) The <u>intensity</u> of the measured wavelength indicates the <u>concentration</u> of that ion in solution. You can work out concentration from intensity using a <u>calibration curve</u>. Here's how...

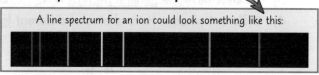

A line spectrum for an ion could look something like this:

 **EXAMPLE:** Flame photometry was carried out on a sample, known to contain calcium ions. The measured wavelength known to be emitted by calcium ions had an emission intensity of 4.5. Use the calibration curve to work out the concentration of calcium ions in the sample.

1) Find the intensity on <u>y-axis</u>.

2) Travel along <u>horizontally</u> from this point, until you reach the <u>curve</u>.

3) Draw a straight line <u>down</u> to the <u>x-axis</u> and read off <u>concentration</u>. So the concentration of calcium ions in the sample is **0.25 mol dm⁻³**.

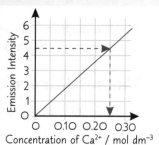

Flame Photometry Works for Mixtures

Flame photometry can also be used to identify different ions in <u>mixtures</u>. This makes it more useful than <u>flame tests</u>, which only work for substances that contain a <u>single metal ion</u>.

For example, a solution containing <u>different</u> ions might give the following spectrum:

You can compare this spectrum against <u>reference spectra</u>:

Spectrum for ion X:

Spectrum for ion Y:

The <u>combination</u> of the spectra for ion X and for ion Y gives the spectrum for the <u>sample</u> tested — this suggests the mixture contains ion **X** and ion **Y**.

Machines can Analyse Unknown Substances

Chemists often use <u>instrumental analysis</u> (i.e tests that use machines), such as flame photometry, <u>instead</u> of conducting tests.

Must identify ions!

<u>Advantages of Using Machines:</u>

• <u>Very sensitive</u> — they can detect even the <u>tiniest amounts</u> of substances.

• <u>Very fast</u> and tests can be automated.

• <u>Very accurate</u> — they don't involve <u>human error</u>, like manual analysis does.

Photometry — it's a flaming useful technique...

So, there you have it — a pretty nifty way to identify different ions. Way cooler than your bog standard flame test.

Q1 Give two advantages of using flame photometry rather than using flame tests to identify ions. [2 marks]

Alkanes and Alkenes

Alkanes and alkenes are dead useful. And all there is to them is some hydrogen and some carbon. Wonderful.

Alkanes are Saturated Hydrocarbons

1) A homologous series is a group of chemicals that have similar chemical structures.

2) Alkanes are a homologous series of hydrocarbons — they contain just carbon and hydrogen atoms.

3) Alkanes have the general formula C_nH_{2n+2}. E.g an alkane with 5 carbons has $(2 \times 5) + 2 = 12$ hydrogens.

4) Different alkanes have chains of different lengths. These are the first four alkanes:

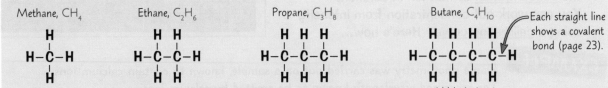

5) The diagrams above show that all the atoms have formed bonds with as many other atoms as they can — this means they're saturated.

Carbon atoms tend to make four bonds, but hydrogen atoms can only make one.

Alkenes Have a C=C Double Bond

This is a carbon-carbon double bond.

1) A functional group is a group of atoms that determine how a molecule reacts. Members of a homologous series all contain the same functional group.

2) Alkenes are a homologous series of hydrocarbons with one C=C functional group. They have the general formula C_nH_{2n} — they have twice as many hydrogens as carbons.

3) They are known as unsaturated because they can make more bonds — the double bond can open up, allowing the two carbon atoms to bond with other atoms.

4) The first three alkenes are ethene, propene, butene (see below).

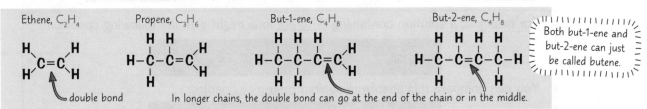

Both but-1-ene and but-2-ene can just be called butene.

In longer chains, the double bond can go at the end of the chain or in the middle.

5) You can test for an alkene using bromine water. When shaken together, an alkene will decolourise bromine water, turning it from orange to colourless. This is because an addition reaction takes place where bromine is added across the alkene double bond. (Alkanes don't react with bromine water as they don't contain double bonds.)

Alkenes also react with steam in addition reactions.

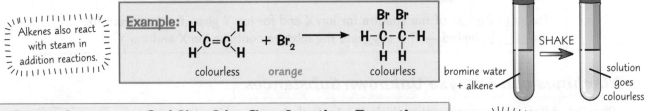

bromine water + alkene

SHAKE

solution goes colourless

Hydrocarbons are Oxidised in Combustion Reactions

In a limited supply of oxygen, you can get incomplete combustion instead (see p.89).

1) Alkanes and alkenes burn in oxygen in combustion reactions.

2) During complete combustion, they're oxidised to form carbon dioxide and water.

$C_2H_6 + 3\frac{1}{2}O_2 \rightarrow 2CO_2 + 3H_2O$	$C_2H_4 + 3O_2 \rightarrow 2CO_2 + 2H_2O$
ethane + oxygen → carbon dioxide + water	ethene + oxygen → carbon dioxide + water

My brain during exam revision is a bit like alkanes — saturated...

Alkanes and alkenes look super similar but that double bond makes a lot of difference — so don't confuse them.

Q1   Draw the structure of propene.   [1 mark]

Addition Polymers

Polymers are made by joining lots of <u>little molecules</u> together in <u>long chains</u>. Magic.

Addition Polymers are Made From Unsaturated Monomers

1) <u>Polymers</u> are substances of <u>high average relative molecular mass</u> made by joining up lots of small repeating units called <u>monomers</u>. The monomers that make up <u>addition polymers</u> have a <u>double covalent bond</u>.

2) Lots of <u>unsaturated monomer molecules</u> (<u>alkenes</u> — see last page) can open up their <u>double bonds</u> and join together to form <u>polymer chains</u>. This is called <u>addition polymerisation</u>.

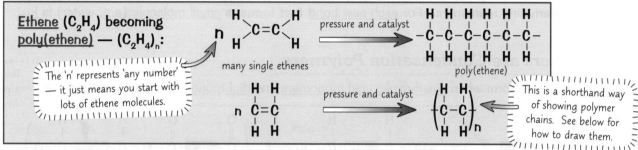

<u>Ethene</u> (C_2H_4) becoming <u>poly(ethene)</u> — ($C_2H_4)_n$:

The 'n' represents 'any number' — it just means you start with lots of ethene molecules.

many single ethenes

pressure and catalyst

poly(ethene)

This is a shorthand way of showing polymer chains. See below for how to draw them.

3) The <u>name</u> of the polymer comes from the <u>type of monomer</u> it's made from — you just put <u>brackets</u> around it and stick the word "<u>poly</u>" in front of it. So <u>propene</u> becomes <u>poly(propene)</u>, etc.

4) To get the <u>formula</u> of the polymer, you just put the formula of the <u>monomer</u> in brackets and put a little 'n' after it. So C_3H_6 becomes $(C_3H_6)_n$. Simple.

You Can Draw the Repeat Unit of a Polymer

1) Drawing the <u>displayed formula</u> of an <u>addition polymer</u> from the displayed formula of its <u>monomer</u> is easy. Join the carbons together in a <u>row</u> with <u>no</u> double bonds between them, stick a pair of <u>brackets</u> around the repeating bit, and put an '<u>n</u>' after it (to show that there are lots of monomers). You should also draw a bond from each of the two carbons in the chain that pass through the brackets — this shows the chain continues.

Chloroethene   Poly(chloroethene)

2) To get from the <u>displayed formula</u> of the <u>polymer</u> to the displayed formula of the <u>monomer</u>, just do the reverse. Draw out the <u>repeating bit</u> of the polymer, get rid of the two bonds going out through the brackets and put a <u>double bond</u> between the <u>carbons</u>.

Poly(tetrafluoroethene)   Tetrafluoroethene

Properties of Polymers Make Them Suitable for Different Uses

1) <u>Poly(tetrafluoroethene)</u> (PTFE), <u>poly(chloroethene)</u> (PVC), <u>poly(ethene)</u> and <u>poly(propene)</u> are <u>addition polymers</u>.

The properties depend on the arrangement of polymer chains and the forces between them.

2) Each polymer has its own set of <u>properties</u>.

3) The set of properties make them perfect for making certain things. Here are some examples...

Polymer	Properties	Uses
Poly(ethene)	flexible, electrical insulator, cheap	plastic bags, bottles, wire insulation
Poly(propene)	flexible, strong, tough, mouldable	crates, furniture, ropes
Poly(chloroethene) (PVC)	tough, cheap	window frames, water pipes
Poly(tetrafluoroethene) (PTFE)	unreactive, tough, non-stick	non-stick pans, waterproof clothing

Which polymer is good for making a cuppa? Poly(putthekettleon)...

Make sure you know how to draw the displayed formulas of addition polymers from the monomer and vice versa.

Q1   Draw the displayed formula of the polymer that is formed when monomers of propene (shown on the right) are reacted together.

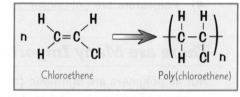

[1 mark]

Condensation Polymers

Condensation polymers? Concentration polymers more like. They're trickier than their addition polymer cousins.

Polymers can be Made by Condensation Polymerisation

1) Condensation polymerisation usually involves two different types of monomer.

2) The monomers react together and bonds form between them, making polymer chains.

3) Each monomer has to contain at least two functional groups, one on each end of the molecule.

4) Each functional group can react with the functional group of another monomer, creating long chains of alternating monomers. For each new bond that forms, a small molecule (e.g. water) is lost.

Polyesters are Condensation Polymers

1) Polyesters form when dicarboxylic acid monomers and diol monomers react together.

> The blocks represent the rest of each molecule.

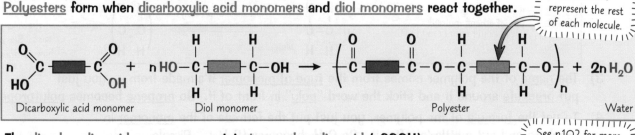

Dicarboxylic acid monomer   Diol monomer   Polyester   Water

> See p.102 for more on alcohols and carboxylic acids.

2) The dicarboxylic acid monomers contain two carboxylic acid (-COOH) groups and the diol monomers contain two alcohol (-OH) groups.

3) When the carboxylic acid group reacts with the alcohol group, it forms an ester link.

4) Polyesters are condensation polymers — each time an ester link is formed, a molecule of water is lost.

There are Many Important Naturally Occurring Polymers

Not all polymers are synthetic (man-made), there are also many polymers that occur naturally — some of which are vital for keeping us alive, such as DNA and proteins. Hurrah for polymers.

1) DNA is a complex molecule that contains genetic information.

2) It contains two strands and each strand is made up of nucleotide monomers that bond together in a polymerisation reaction.

3) DNA is made from four different monomers called nucleotides.

1) Amino acid monomers form polymers known as proteins via condensation polymerisation.

2) Proteins have many important uses in the human body, e.g. in enzymes (see page 82).

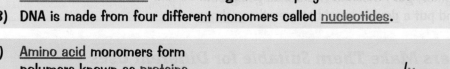

Amino acid monomer   Protein

1) Carbohydrates are molecules containing carbon, oxygen and hydrogen, used by living things to produce energy.

2) Starch and cellulose are large, complex carbohydrates, which are made up of many smaller units of carbohydrates, known as sugars, joined together in a long chain.

The conga — a naturally occurring polymer at weddings.

Revision's like polymers — it's all about stringing facts together...

...and can go on and on and on and on. Best try some revision now and see if you can answer the questions below.

Q1   Name the two types of monomer that react together to form polyesters.   [1 mark]

Q2   How is the molecule of water formed when polyesters are made?   [1 mark]

Disposing of Polymers

It's easy to throw away old plastic bottles and plastic packaging without giving much thought — but we need to start thinking about the <u>impact</u> it's having on the <u>environment</u> today and the <u>availability</u> of plastics in the future.

Polymers are Made From Crude Oil

1) <u>Plastics</u> are a type of <u>polymer</u> which are made from <u>crude oil</u>. Crude oil is a <u>finite</u> resource — eventually, it will all get used up and run out.

2) The more we use up our crude oil resources, the more <u>expensive</u> crude oil will become — this will then <u>increase the price</u> of crude oil products.

3) Crude oil isn't just used to make <u>plastics</u> — we need it for lots of different things, such as petrol for cars and heating our homes. As resources dry up, we will face the dilemma of how to use the remaining oil. One way we can help delay this problem is by <u>recycling</u> our polymers.

The Disposal of Polymers Comes with Many Problems

In the UK, over <u>2 million</u> tonnes of plastic waste are generated each year. It's important to find ways to get rid of this waste while <u>minimising environmental damage</u>.

<u>Disposal of Polymers in Landfill Sites:</u>

1) A lot of plastics get dumped in <u>landfill sites</u>. This is usually when different polymers are too <u>difficult</u> or <u>expensive</u> to <u>separate</u> and recycle.

2) Lots of <u>valuable land</u> is quickly getting used up for use as landfill sites.

3) Most polymers are <u>non-biodegradable</u> — they're not broken down by microorganisms. This means that they will sit in landfill for years and years and years and years...

<u>Disposal of Polymers by Combustion:</u>

1) <u>Burning plastics</u> produces a lot of <u>energy</u> and this can be used to <u>generate electricity</u>. But it's not all rainbows and smiles...

2) If not carefully controlled, <u>toxic gases</u> can be released from the combustion of plastics. For example, when polymers that contain chlorine (such as PVC) are burned, they produce HCl — this has to be removed.

3) <u>Carbon dioxide</u> is also produced and this contributes to <u>global warming</u>.

Recycling Polymers Has Both Pros and Cons

1) <u>Recycling</u> polymers is a great way to limit the amount of crude oil we're using and avoid the <u>environmental impact</u> of burning and landfills.

2) Unfortunately, recycling is not as <u>simple</u> as throwing all the plastic rubbish together and then melting and remoulding it all...

Stop trying to recycle your brother, Mark.

ADVANTAGES	DISADVANTAGES
• <u>Reduces</u> the amount of <u>non-biodegradable</u> waste filling up landfill sites. • <u>Reduces emissions</u> of greenhouse and toxic gases which can be released from burning polymers. • Recycling generally uses up <u>less water</u> and <u>energy resources</u> than when making new plastics. • <u>Reduces</u> the amount of <u>crude oil</u> needed to produce more plastics. • Recycling generally <u>saves money</u> and <u>creates jobs</u>.	• Polymers must be <u>separated</u> by type before they can be <u>melted</u> and <u>reformed</u> into a new product — this can be <u>difficult</u> and <u>expensive</u>. • If polymers are <u>mixed</u> together, the <u>quality</u> of the final recycled polymer product could be <u>reduced</u>. • Polymers can only be recycled a <u>finite</u> number of times. Over time, the <u>strength</u> of the polymer can decrease. • Melting down polymers can release dangerous gases into the atmosphere. These are <u>harmful</u> to plants and animals.

I hear plastic cars are the way forward — they don't break down...

So, if you didn't realise how important recycling polymers was, you should definitely know now. I, for one, can't imagine a life without plastics or petrol, but if we carry on they way we are going, it could soon become reality...

Q1   Give two disadvantages of burning waste plastics. [2 marks]

Q2   Explain why the price of polymer products could increase if we don't recycle polymers. [3 marks]

Alcohols and Carboxylic Acids

This page is about different types of alcohol — and that's not just beer, wine and other pub favourites...

Alcohols Have an '-OH' Functional Group and End in '-ol'

1) The general formula of an alcohol is $C_nH_{2n+1}OH$. So an alcohol with 2 carbons has the formula C_2H_5OH.

2) All alcohols contain an -OH functional group. Here are the first four alcohols in the homologous series:

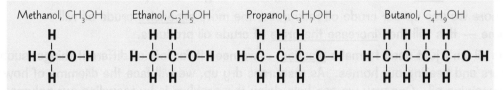

3) The basic naming system is the same as for alkanes — but replace the final '-e' with '-ol'.

4) Don't write CH_4O instead of CH_3OH — it doesn't show the functional -OH group.

5) It is possible to get alcohols where the -OH group is attached to different carbon atoms in the carbon chain, or alcohols with more than one -OH group (like the ones that form condensation polymers on page 100).

6) If you heat a mixture of an alcohol and an acid catalyst, an alkene and water are formed. This is called a dehydration reaction, because a molecule of water is lost from the alcohol for each alkene molecule formed.

Alcohols Can Be Oxidised to Form Carboxylic Acids

1) When something's oxidised, it gains oxygen.

2) Alcohols can be oxidised to form carboxylic acids using an oxidising agent.

Example: Ethanol + an oxidising agent.

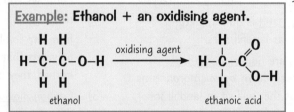

Oxidation can also describe the loss of electrons (see page 54).

Alcohols can only form carboxylic acids in this way if the -OH group is attached to a carbon that's only attached to one carbon itself.

3) Solutions of carboxylic acids have properties that they share with other acids. For example:
   • They react like other acids. E.g. they react with carbonates to produce carbon dioxide, a salt and water.
   • In solution, they can partially ionise and release H^+ ions, which make the solution weakly acidic.

4) The basic naming system for carboxylic acids is the same as for alkanes — but replace the final '-e' with '-oic acid'.

5) Carboxylic acids are another homologous series of molecules. They have the general formula $C_{n-1}H_{2n-1}COOH$ and they have a -COOH functional group.

6) Here are the first four carboxylic acids in the homologous series. They can each be formed by oxidising the alcohol which contains the same total number of carbons (i.e. methanol is oxidised to methanoic acid, ethanol is oxidised to ethanoic acid, and so on).

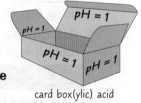

card box(ylic) acid

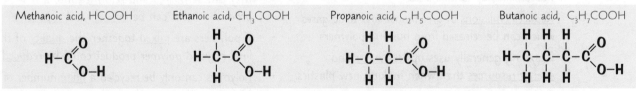

7) Remember — members of a homologous series have similar reactions because they contain the same functional group. So if you know how a certain molecule in a homologous series reacts (e.g. ethanol forming ethanoic acid), you can predict how other molecules in that series react.

At every firework display, there's an -OH group and an -AH group...

Two more homologous series for you. Let's see if you've got them sussed with some practice questions.

Q1 An alcohol has the formula CH_3OH. What is the name of this alcohol? [1 mark]

Q2 A chemist reacts an oxidising agent with an unknown alcohol and forms propanoic acid. Name the alcohol that the chemist started with. [1 mark]

Production of Ethanol

People have been discovering new chemicals for years. <u>Ethanol</u> was discovered <u>thousands of years ago</u>.

Ethanol can be Made by Fermentation

1) <u>Fermentation</u> is the process of using <u>yeast</u> to convert a type of <u>carbohydrate</u> called sugars into <u>alcohol</u>.

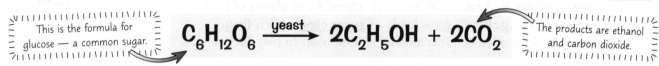

This is the formula for glucose — a common sugar.

$$C_6H_{12}O_6 \xrightarrow{\text{yeast}} 2C_2H_5OH + 2CO_2$$

The products are ethanol and carbon dioxide.

2) The carbohydrate can come from any source, but the <u>sugar cane</u> and <u>sugar beet</u> plants are often used.

3) Yeast cells contain an <u>enzyme</u>. Enzymes are naturally occurring <u>catalysts</u> (see page 82) — they speed up reactions.

Ethanol is an alcohol (see previous page).

4) Here's how you would <u>make</u> a <u>solution of ethanol</u> by fermentation:

   - Mix <u>yeast</u> and a solution of a <u>carbohydrate</u> (e.g. glucose) in a clean container. <u>Seal</u> the container and leave it in a <u>warm place</u>.

   - Keep the mixture between <u>30 °C</u> and <u>40 °C</u> — fermentation happens <u>fastest</u> between these temperatures. At lower temperatures, the reaction slows down. If it's <u>too hot</u> the enzyme in the yeast <u>denatures</u> (is destroyed) and the reaction would stop.

   - It's important to keep the mixture in <u>anaerobic conditions</u> (no oxygen). Oxygen converts the <u>ethanol</u> to <u>ethanoic acid</u> (which is what you get in <u>vinegar</u> — it doesn't exactly enhance the drinking experience).

   - When the <u>concentration</u> of alcohol reaches about 10 to 20%, the fermentation reaction <u>stops</u>, because the yeast gets <u>killed off</u> by the alcohol.

   - The yeast will fall to the <u>bottom</u> of the container — you can collect the <u>ethanol solution</u> from the <u>top</u>.

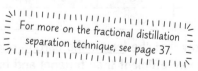

5) The fermented mixture can be <u>distilled</u> (see below) to produce more concentrated alcohol. Brandy is distilled from wine, whisky is distilled from fermented grain and vodka's distilled from fermented grain or potatoes.

6) Different types of alcoholic drink contain <u>different percentages</u> of ethanol. The typical ethanol concentration of <u>beer</u> is about <u>4%</u> whilst some <u>spirits</u> have a concentration of <u>40%</u>.

Fractional Distillation is Used to Concentrate Ethanol

1) A <u>dilute solution</u> of ethanol is produced by fermentation.

2) To make a concentration of ethanol above 20%, ethanol must be <u>concentrated</u> by <u>fractional distillation</u> of the fermentation mixture. Fractional distillation separates mixtures by heating them.

3) Ethanol has a <u>lower</u> boiling point than <u>water</u>. This means that when the fermentation mixture is heated, <u>ethanol evaporates</u> and the vapour rises up the fractionating column, while the <u>water</u> stays as a <u>liquid</u>.

4) A Liebig condenser is used to <u>condense</u> the ethanol vapour by cooling it. The concentrated ethanol can then be collected in a separate flask.

For more on the fractional distillation separation technique, see page 37.

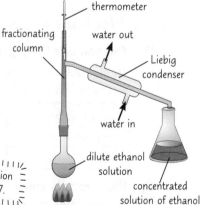

thermometer

fractionating column

water out

Liebig condenser

water in

dilute ethanol solution

concentrated solution of ethanol

Keep your spirits up, don't wine, beer positive...

I quite like this page. Well, maybe not the whole page. I just like the fact that I'm at the end of the page actually...

Q1   Name the type of molecule which is converted to ethanol by fermentation.   [1 mark]

Q2   Explain why a temperature between 30 °C and 40 °C is used in the fermentation process.   [2 marks]

Q3   What is the purpose of fractional distillation during the manufacture of ethanol?   [1 mark]

Combustion of Alcohols

Yay, another experiment. This one looks at how effectively different <u>alcohols</u> work as <u>fuels</u>.

Alcohols can be Used as Fuels

1) <u>Alcohols</u> can be used for <u>fuel</u> because when they're <u>burned</u>, they release <u>energy</u>.

2) Some countries that have little or no oil deposits but plenty of land and sunshine (e.g. Brazil) grow loads of <u>sugar cane</u>, which they <u>ferment</u> to form ethanol. This ethanol is then used to help fuel cars.

Alcohol can be Burned to Heat Up Water

Some alcohols are <u>better fuels</u> than others. To see which alcohol is best, you can do an experiment using different alcohols to heat up a specific volume of water.

PRACTICAL

1) Put some alcohol into a <u>spirit burner</u> and measure the <u>mass</u> of the burner and fuel using a <u>mass balance</u>.

Alcohols are hazardous to humans — e.g. methanol is toxic and propanol is an irritant — so you should make sure you're wearing gloves and safety glasses.

2) Measure 100 cm³ <u>distilled water</u> into a <u>copper calorimeter</u> (use the same container for each experiment).

3) <u>Insulate</u> the calorimeter by using a <u>draught excluder</u>, then cover with an <u>insulating lid</u> after placing a <u>thermometer</u> inside. This helps to make sure that minimal energy is lost to the surroundings.

4) Take the <u>initial temperature</u> of the water then put the burner under the calorimeter and <u>light the wick</u>.

Alcohol is highly flammable so direct contact with the flame should be avoided - just light the wick.

5) <u>Stir</u> the water throughout using the thermometer. When the heat from the burner has made the temperature of the water rise by <u>20 °C</u>, blow out the spirit burner.

The apparatus will get hot during the experiment, so you should allow it to cool before touching it, or use tongs.

6) Immediately <u>reweigh</u> the burner and fuel.

7) <u>Repeat</u> the experiment using other alcohols but make sure that you keep all other variables the <u>same</u> for each experiment, including the:
- <u>mass/volume</u> of water,
- <u>height</u> of the container above the wick,
- <u>length</u> of the wick / <u>height</u> of the flame,
- number of <u>moles</u> of alcohol.

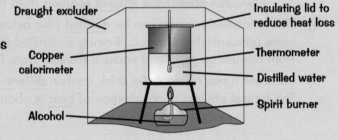

Draught excluder — Copper calorimeter — Alcohol — Insulating lid to reduce heat loss — Thermometer — Distilled water — Spirit burner

Less Alcohol Burned Means a Better Fuel

1) You can use the <u>results</u> from your experiment to <u>compare the efficiency of alcohols as fuels</u>.

2) An alcohol will be more <u>efficient</u> as a fuel compared to another alcohol if less fuel is needed to raise the temperature of the water by a given amount.

	Ethanol	Propanol	Butanol	Pentanol
Temperature rise (°C)	20	20	20	20
Mass of fuel used (g)	0.48	0.39	0.34	0.28

Less pentanol, $C_5H_{11}OH$, is needed to heat the water by 20 °C compared to the mass of ethanol, C_2H_5OH, needed.

3) These results show that the <u>longer the carbon chain</u> of the alcohol, the <u>more efficient</u> the fuel will be. So, pentanol is more efficient than butanol and butanol is more efficient than propanol.

Spirit burners — warding off poltergeists since 1268...

To keep it a fair test, it's important to keep all variables exactly the same, only changing the type of alcohol used, otherwise you might think that an alcohol is more efficient but it could just be that the flame is closer to the water.

Q1 The combustion of 1.92 g of alcohol X raised the temperature of a set volume of water in a copper calorimeter by 25 °C. It took 1.46 g of alcohol Y to raise the temperature of the same volume of water by the same amount. Which alcohol, X or Y, is more efficient? [1 mark]

Nanoparticles

Time for some properly cutting-edge science now. Nanoparticles have loads of really useful properties and new uses for them are being developed all the time.

Nanoparticles are Really Really Really Really Tiny

1) Really tiny particles, 1–100 nanometers across, are called 'nanoparticles' (1 nm = 0.000 000 001 m). Nanoparticles contain roughly a few hundred atoms — so they're bigger than atoms (atoms are around 0.1–0.5 nm) and simple molecules, but smaller than pretty much anything else.

2) Fullerenes are nanoparticles. The fullerenes include nanotubes (see page 24), tiny hollow carbon tubes. All those covalent bonds make carbon nanotubes very strong.

3) A nanoparticle has very different properties from the 'bulk' chemical that it's made from — e.g. fullerenes have different properties from big lumps of carbon.

For more on fullerenes, see page 24.

Nanoparticles Have a High Surface Area to Volume Ratio

1) As particles decrease in size, the size of their surface area increases in relation to their volume — so their surface area to volume ratio increases.

surface area to volume ratio = surface area ÷ volume

2) Nanoparticles have a really high surface area to volume ratio compared to larger particles.

3) This gives them different properties from larger particles, because a much greater proportion of their atoms are available to interact with substances they come into contact with.

Nanoparticles Can Modify the Properties of Materials

Using nanoparticles is known as nanoscience. Many new uses of nanoparticles are being developed:

• They have a huge surface area to volume ratio, so they can make good catalysts (see p.82). This is because reactions take place on the surface of catalysts, so the bigger the surface area, the more collisions there will be and so the faster the rate of reaction.

• New cosmetics, e.g. sunscreens, have been made using nanoparticles. The small particles provide better protection but don't leave white marks on the skin.

• Nanomedicine is a hot topic. The idea is that tiny fullerenes are absorbed more easily by the body than most particles. This means they could deliver drugs right into the cells where they're needed.

• New lubricant coatings using fullerenes could be used in, e.g. artificial joints and gears.

• Nanotubes conduct electricity, so they can be used in tiny electric circuits for computer chips.

• Nanoparticles are added to plastics in sports equipment, e.g. tennis rackets, golf clubs and golf balls. They make the plastic much stronger and more durable, without adding much mass (hardly any at all).

• Silver nanoparticles are added to the polymer fibres used to make surgical masks and wound dressings. This gives the fibres antibacterial properties.

The Effects of Nanoparticles on Health Aren't Fully Understood

1) Although nanoparticles are useful, the way they affect the body isn't fully understood, so it's important that any new products are tested thoroughly to minimise the risks.

The large surface area to volume ratio could be making them more toxic.

2) Some people are worried that products containing nanoparticles have been made available before any possible harmful effects on human health have been investigated properly — in other words, we don't know what the side effects or long-term impacts on health could be.

3) For example, some nanoparticles used in medicine don't break down easily so they could start to build up in cells. They could also cause problems such as lung inflammation if they're breathed in.

Nanofarticles — when ants get into that old tin of baked beans...

It seems like small particles are big business — but as with any new tech there are pros and cons. Make sure you've got a handle on why nanoparticles act differently from big particles.

Q1   Give three examples of uses of nanoparticles.   [3 marks]

Types of Materials

The <u>properties</u> of materials are all to do with the <u>bonding</u> in them. Look back at pages 21-25 for more about different types of bonding and how this affects something's properties. Now, more on properties. Lucky you.

There are Lots of Different Types of Polymer

Polymerisation reactions involving <u>different monomers</u> can be used to make a <u>wide range</u> of polymers. Different polymers have different <u>physical properties</u> — some are <u>stronger</u>, <u>stretchier</u>, more <u>easily moulded</u>, and so on. These physical properties make them suited for <u>different uses</u>:

See pages 99-100 for more on polymers.

<u>Strong, rigid</u> polymers such as <u>high-density poly(ethene)</u> are used to make water pipes.
<u>Light, stretchy</u> polymers such as <u>low-density poly(ethene)</u> are used for plastic bags and squeezy bottles.
<u>Poly(styrene) foam</u> is used in <u>packaging</u> to protect breakable things, and as a <u>thermal insulator</u>.
<u>Heat-resistant</u> polymers such as <u>melamine</u> resin and <u>poly(propene)</u> are used to make <u>plastic kettles</u>.

Ceramics are Stiff but Brittle

Ceramics include glass, porcelain and bone china.

<u>Ceramics</u> are made by baking substances, such as clay, to produce a <u>brittle</u>, <u>stiff</u> material.

*   <u>Clay</u> is a mineral formed from <u>weathered</u> and <u>decomposed rock</u>. It's <u>soft</u> when it's <u>dug up</u> out of the ground, which makes it <u>easy to mould</u> into different shapes required for pottery or bricks.
*   It can be <u>hardened</u> by firing at very <u>high temperatures</u>. This makes it <u>ideal</u> as a <u>building</u> material — clay bricks can <u>withstand</u> the <u>weight</u> of lots <u>more bricks</u> on top of them.

*   <u>Glass</u> is generally <u>transparent</u> and <u>strong</u>, can be <u>moulded</u> when hot and can be <u>brittle</u> when thin.
*   The majority of glass made is <u>soda-lime glass</u> which is made by heating <u>limestone</u>, <u>sand</u> and <u>sodium carbonate</u> (soda) until they melt. When the mixture cools it comes out as <u>glass</u>.

Composites are Made of Different Materials

Composites, such as <u>fibreglass</u> and <u>concrete</u>, are made of one material (the reinforcement) <u>embedded</u> in another (the matrix/binder). The <u>properties</u> of a composite depend on the properties of the materials it is <u>made from</u>. For example:

<u>Carbon fibre</u> composites have been made using carbon atoms bonded together to make carbon fibres or carbon <u>nanotubes</u> (see p.24) held together in a polymer resin matrix. These polymers are expensive to make but are very <u>strong</u> and <u>light</u> making them ideal for use in aerospace and sports car manufacturing.

Metals are Good Conductors

See page 25 for more on metals and page 63 for more on alloys.

Metals are generally very good at <u>conducting</u> both <u>heat</u> and <u>electricity</u>. They typically have a <u>high density</u> and are <u>malleable</u>. Metals can also be <u>mixed</u> with other elements to form <u>alloys</u>.

Different Materials have Different Properties

Each type of material has a <u>different</u> set of <u>physical properties</u>. You can compare these properties to see what material would be <u>best</u> for making a certain product (see next page). For example, the data below tells you that <u>HDPE</u> has a <u>low tensile strength</u> (it breaks easily) and is <u>less dense</u> than soda-lime glass, a carbon fibre composite and aluminium...

	HDPE	Soda-lime glass	Carbon fibre composite	Aluminium
Tensile Strength (MPa)	37	19 – 77	1860	90
Density (g cm^{-3})	0.94 – 0.97	2.44	1.50	2.70

My best mate is made from glass, I have a smashing time with him...

So many materials, but my favourite type of material will always be the soft, fluffy kind...

Q1   Name two composite materials. [2 marks]

Materials and their Uses

It's all very well making a material but it needs to be fit for purpose. You need to be able to understand <u>why</u> a certain material is used and <u>not</u> another material. For example, a kettle made of melamine instead of chocolate.

Different Materials are Suited to Different Jobs

What materials are used for depends on their <u>properties</u>. In the <u>exam</u> they might ask you to <u>interpret information</u> about the properties of materials and <u>assess</u> the <u>suitability</u> of these materials for different purposes.

> You should know all about the bonding in metals (see page 25) and polymers (see pages 99-100).

<u>Polymers</u> are really adaptable — for example, they're often <u>flexible</u>, so they can be bent without breaking, and can be <u>easily moulded</u> into almost any shape. They're often <u>cheaper</u> than most other materials, and they also tend to be <u>less dense</u> than most metals or ceramics, so they're often used when designing products that need to have a low mass. They're also <u>thermal</u> and <u>electrical insulators</u>. Polymers can <u>degrade</u> and <u>break down</u> over time, so polymer products don't always last as long as those made from other materials.

<u>Ceramics</u>, like polymers, are <u>insulators</u> of heat and electricity. They're much more <u>brittle</u> and <u>stiff</u> than most other materials, but they're also <u>strong</u> and <u>hard wearing</u>. They don't <u>degrade</u> or <u>corrode</u> like other materials can, so they last a lot longer — that's why we still use glass in windows instead of clear plastic.

<u>Metals</u> are <u>good conductors</u> of <u>heat</u> and <u>electricity</u> — which can be an advantage or a disadvantage, depending on what the material is needed for. They're <u>malleable</u>, so like polymers they can be formed into a variety of shapes. Some metals corrode easily, but products made from <u>corrosion resistant</u> metals can last for a very long time. Metals are usually <u>less brittle</u> than either ceramics or polymers, so they're likely to <u>deform</u> but stay in one piece where other materials may <u>shatter</u>.

<u>Composites</u> have different properties depending on the <u>matrix/binder</u> and the <u>reinforcement</u>. The combination of <u>component materials</u> used can be altered, so composites can be designed to have specific properties for a <u>specific purpose</u>. The main <u>disadvantage</u> of composites is that they tend to be much more <u>expensive</u> to produce than other materials.

You Need to Be Able to Interpret Information about Materials

You can <u>use information</u> about the properties of materials and <u>assess</u> their <u>suitability</u> for different uses.

EXAMPLE: A company is investigating the best material to make a fencing sword. The sword needs to be strong and lightweight, and is intended to be sold mainly to beginners to the sport of fencing. Using the data in the table, suggest which material from the table the company should use.

Material	Density (g cm⁻³)	Strength (MPa)	Cost
Steel	7.8	780	Low
Poly(propene)	0.94	48	Low
Copper	8.9	220	Medium
Carbon Fibre	1.5	4100	High

Poly(propene) can be ruled out — it's cheap and light but a lot weaker than all the other options.
Copper's heavier, weaker and more expensive than steel, so it can't be the best option.
Carbon fibre is really strong and light, but it's also expensive.
This is a sword for beginners, so the price should be kept down.
Steel swords will have a fairly high strength relative to their weight and would be cheap to make. So **steel** is the best material for the job.

As well as making sure a product is <u>fit for its purpose</u>, <u>life cycle assessment data</u> (see page 58) is also used to work out how <u>environmentally friendly</u> the manufacture, use and disposal of a product is.

Compost-sites — piles of old vegetables embedded in muck...

So, you can't use any old material for any old job. My steel pillow and my glass duvet taught me that.

Q1 Look at the table in the example above. Given that poly(propene) and carbon fibre are poor thermal conductors, steel is a good thermal conductor and copper is a very good thermal conductor, which of the four materials would you use to make an insulating coffee flask? Explain your answer. [3 marks]

Revision Questions for Topic 9

Woohoo — you did it. Just a few more questions to go, then I think a cup of tea and a digestive are in order.
- Try these questions and tick off each one when you get it right.
- When you've done all the questions under a heading and are completely happy with it, tick off the topic.

Tests for Ions (p.95-97) ☑

1) What colour flame is produced when calcium is heated in a flame? ☑
2) What gas will turn damp, red litmus paper blue? ☑
3) Describe how you would test a solution for sulfate ions. ☑
4) In flame photometry, what does the intensity of the light at the measured wavelength show? ☑

Alkanes and Alkenes (p.98) ☑

5) What elements do alkanes contain? ☑
6) Name the alkene that contains six hydrogen atoms. ☑
7) Outline how you could you test to see if a solution contains an alkene. ☑
8) Name the products that would be formed if an alkane was burned in a good supply of oxygen. ☑

Polymers (p.99-101) ☑

9) What functional group does a monomer need to form addition polymers? ☑
10) List three properties of poly(ethene). ☑
11) Draw a block diagram to represent a polyester. ☑
12) Name the type of monomers that form DNA. ☑
13) Give a disadvantage associated with the disposal of polymers in landfills. ☑
14) Why do polymers need to be separated before they can be recycled? ☑

Alcohols and Carboxylic Acids (p.102-104) ☑

15) What is the chemical formula for butanol? ☑
16) Name the product formed when ethanol is oxidised by an oxidising agent. ☑
17) Name the carboxylic acid with the chemical formula C_2H_5COOH. ☑
18) Draw a diagram of the equipment you would use to concentrate a solution of dilute ethanol. ☑
19) Explain why it is important to insulate the copper calorimeter when carrying out an experiment comparing the efficiency of different alcohols as fuels. ☑
20) Which alcohol would be a more efficient fuel — methanol or propanol? ☑

Nanoparticles and Types of Materials (p.105-107) ☑

21) How big are nanoparticles? ☑
22) Explain why a high surface area to volume ratio gives nanoparticles different properties to larger particles. ☑
23) Why are nanoparticles good for making sunscreens? ☑
24) Give two properties of ceramics. ☑
25) Name the type of material that is a good electrical conductor. ☑
26) Give the main disadvantage associated with using composite materials instead of other types of material. ☑

Practical Techniques

* This section covers <u>practical skills</u> you'll need to know about for your course.
* You'll have to do <u>8 core practicals</u> (experiments). These are covered earlier in the book and they're <u>highlighted</u> with <u>practical stamps</u> like this one.
* The following pages of this section cover some <u>extra bits and bobs</u> you need to know about practical work. First up, using apparatus to take measurements...

PRACTICAL

Solids Should Be Measured Using a Balance

1) To weigh a solid, start by putting the <u>container</u> you're weighing your substance <u>into</u> on the <u>balance</u>.

2) Set the balance to exactly <u>zero</u> and then start weighing out your substance.

3) It's <u>no good</u> carefully weighing out your solid if it's not all transferred to your reaction vessel — the amount in the <u>reaction vessel</u> won't be the same as your measurement. Here's a couple of methods you can use to make sure that none gets left in your weighing container...

> * If you're <u>dissolving</u> the solid in a solvent to make a <u>solution</u>, you could <u>wash</u> any remaining solid into the new container using the <u>solvent</u>. This way you know that <u>all</u> the solid you weighed has been transferred.
>
> * You could set the balance <u>to zero</u> before you put your <u>weighing container</u> on the balance. Then <u>reweigh</u> the weighing container <u>after</u> you've transferred the substance. Use the <u>difference</u> in mass to work out <u>exactly</u> how much solid you've transferred.

Three Ways to Measure Liquids

There are a few methods you might use to measure the volume of a liquid. Whichever method you use, always read the volume from the <u>bottom of the meniscus</u> (the curved upper surface of the liquid) when it's at <u>eye level</u>.

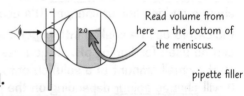

Read volume from here — the bottom of the meniscus.

pipette filler

> <u>Pipettes</u> are long, narrow tubes that are used to suck up an <u>accurate</u> volume of liquid and <u>transfer</u> it to another container. A <u>pipette filler</u> attached to the end of the pipette is used so that you can <u>safely control</u> the amount of liquid you're drawing up. Pipettes are often <u>calibrated</u> to allow for the fact that the last drop of liquid stays in the pipette when the liquid is ejected. This reduces <u>transfer errors</u>.

> <u>Burettes</u> measure from top to bottom (so when they're filled to the top of the scale, the scale reads zero). They have a tap at the bottom which you can use to release the liquid into another container (you can even release it drop by drop). To use a burette, take an <u>initial reading</u>, and once you've released as much liquid as you want, take a <u>final reading</u>. The <u>difference</u> between the readings tells you <u>how much</u> liquid you used.

Burettes are used a lot for titrations. There's loads more about titrations on page 65.

> <u>Measuring cylinders</u> are the most common way to measure out a liquid. They come in all different <u>sizes</u>. Make sure you choose one that's the right size for the measurement you want to make. It's no good using a huge 1000 cm^3 cylinder to measure out 2 cm^3 of a liquid — the graduations will be too big, and you'll end up with <u>massive errors</u>. It'd be much better to use one that measures up to 10 cm^3.

If you only want a couple of drops of liquid, and don't need it to be accurately measured, you can use a dropping pipette to transfer it. For example, this is how you'd add a couple of drops of indicator into a mixture.

Gas Syringes Measure Gas Volumes

Gases can be measured with a gas syringe. They should be measured at <u>room temperature and pressure</u> as the <u>volume</u> of a gas <u>changes</u> with temperature and pressure. You should also use a gas syringe that's the <u>right size</u> for the measurement you're making. Before you use the syringe, you should make sure it's completely sealed and that the plunger moves smoothly.

Practical Techniques

Measure Temperature Accurately

You can use a thermometer to measure the temperature of a substance:

1) Make sure the bulb of your thermometer is completely submerged in any mixture you're measuring.
2) If you're taking an initial reading, you should wait for the temperature to stabilise first.
3) Read your measurement off the scale on a thermometer at eye level to make sure it's correct.

You May Have to Measure the Time Taken for a Change

1) You should use a stopwatch to time experiments. These measure to the nearest 0.1 s so are accurate.
2) Always make sure you start and stop the stopwatch at exactly the right time. For example, if you're investigating the rate of an experiment, you should start timing at the exact moment you mix the reagents and start the reaction. If you're measuring the time taken for a precipitate to form, you should watch the reaction like a hawk so you can stop timing the moment it goes cloudy.

Measure pH to Find Out How Acidic or Alkaline a Solution Is

You need to be able to decide the best method for measuring pH, depending on what your experiment is.

1) Indicators are dyes that change colour depending on whether they're in an acid or an alkali. You use them by adding a couple of drops of the indicator to the solution you're interested in. They're useful for titration reactions, when you want to find the point at which a solution is neutralised.

2) Universal indicator is a mixture of indicators that changes colour gradually as pH changes. It doesn't show a sudden colour change. It's useful for estimating the pH of a solution based on its colour.

3) Indicators can be soaked into paper and strips of this paper can be used for testing pH. If you use a dropping pipette to spot a small amount of a solution onto some indicator paper, it will change colour depending on the pH of the solution.

> Litmus paper turns red in acidic conditions and blue in basic conditions. Universal indicator paper can be used to estimate the pH based on its colour.

4) Indicator paper is useful when you don't want to change the colour of all of the substance, or if the substance is already coloured so might obscure the colour of the indicator. You can also hold a piece of damp indicator paper in a gas sample to test its pH.

5) pH probes are attached to pH meters which have a digital display that gives a numerical value for the pH of a solution. They're used to give an accurate value of pH.

There's loads more about pH on page 43.

Be Careful When You Handle or Mix Substances

1) There are lots of hazards in chemistry experiments, so before you start any experiment, you should read any safety precautions to do with your method or the chemicals you're using.

2) The substances used in chemical reactions are often hazardous. For example, they might catch fire easily (they're flammable), or they might irritate or burn your skin if you come into contact with them.

3) Whenever you're doing an experiment, you should wear a lab coat, safety goggles and gloves.

4) Always be careful that the chemicals you're using aren't flammable before you go lighting any Bunsen burners, and make sure you're working in an area that's well ventilated.

5) If you're doing an experiment that might produce nasty gases (such as chlorine), you should carry out the experiment in a fume hood so that the gas can't escape out into the room you're working in.

6) Never directly touch any chemicals (even if you're wearing gloves). Use a spatula to transfer solids between containers. Carefully pour liquids between different containers, using a funnel to avoid spillages.

7) Be careful when you're mixing chemicals, as a reaction might occur. If you're diluting a liquid, add the concentrated substance to the water (not the other way around) or the mixture could get very hot.

The Tempipettes and MacBurette — Shakespeare for chemists...

It's no good throwing chemicals around willy nilly and calling it an experiment. To make sure your results are reproducible, so can be trusted by other scientists, you have to make sure all your measurements are accurate.

Setting Up Equipment

Setting up the equipment for an experiment correctly is <u>just as important</u> as making accurate measurements.

To Collect Gases, the System Needs to be Sealed

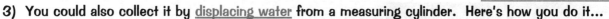

1) There are times when you might want to <u>collect</u> the gas produced by a reaction. For example, to investigate the <u>rate</u> of reaction.

2) The most accurate way to measure the volume of a gas that's been produced is to collect it in a <u>gas syringe</u> (see page 109).

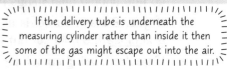

delivery tube — *collected gas* — *gas syringe* — *reaction mixture*

3) You could also collect it by <u>displacing water</u> from a measuring cylinder. Here's how you do it...

- Fill a <u>measuring cylinder</u> with <u>water</u>, and carefully place it <u>upside down</u> in a container of water. Record the <u>initial level</u> of the water in the measuring cylinder.

- Position a <u>delivery tube</u> coming <u>from</u> the reaction vessel so that it's <u>inside</u> the measuring cylinder, pointing upwards. Any gas that's produced will pass <u>through</u> the delivery tube and <u>into</u> the <u>measuring cylinder</u>. As the gas enters the measuring cylinder, the <u>water</u> is <u>pushed out</u>.

delivery tube — *collected gas* — *measuring cylinder filled with water and upturned in a beaker of water* — *reaction mixture*

- Record the <u>level of water</u> in the measuring cylinder and use this value, along with your <u>initial value</u>, to calculate the <u>volume</u> of gas produced.

4) When you're measuring a gas, your equipment has to be <u>sealed</u> or some gas could escape and your results wouldn't be <u>accurate</u>.

If the delivery tube is underneath the measuring cylinder rather than inside it then some of the gas might escape out into the air.

5) If just want to <u>collect</u> a sample to test (and don't need to measure a volume), you can collect it over water as above using a <u>test tube</u>. Once the test tube is full of gas, you can stopper it and store the gas for later.

You May Have to Identify the Products of Electrolysis

There's more about electrolysis on pages 48-50.

1) When you electrolyse an <u>aqueous solution</u>, the products of electrolysis will depend on how reactive the ions in the solution are compared to the H^+ and OH^- ions that come from water.

2) At the <u>cathode</u> you'll either get a <u>pure metal</u> coating the electrode or bubbles of <u>hydrogen gas</u>.

3) At the <u>anode</u>, you'll get bubbles of <u>oxygen gas</u> unless a <u>halide ion</u> is present, when you'll get the <u>halogen</u>.

4) You may have to predict and identify what's been made in an electrolysis experiment. To do this, you need to be able to <u>set up the equipment</u> correctly so that you can <u>collect</u> any gas that's produced. The easiest way to collect the gas is in a <u>test tube</u>.

5) Here's how to set up the equipment...

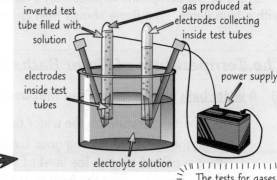

inverted test tube filled with solution — *gas produced at electrodes collecting inside test tubes* — *electrodes inside test tubes* — *power supply* — *electrolyte solution*

The tests for gases are described on pages 45, 74, 91 and 95.

Make Sure You Can Draw Diagrams of Your Equipment

When you're writing out a <u>method</u> for your experiment, it's always a good idea to draw a <u>labelled diagram</u> showing how your apparatus will be <u>set up</u>. The easiest way to do this is to use a scientific drawing, where each piece of apparatus is drawn as if you're looking at its <u>cross-section</u>. For example:

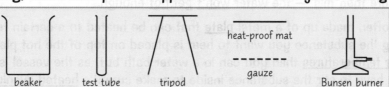

beaker — *test tube* — *tripod* — *heat-proof mat* — *gauze* — *Bunsen burner*

The pieces of glassware are drawn without tops so they aren't sealed. If you want to draw a closed system, remember to draw a bung in the top.

I set up my equipment — they had a blind date at the cinema...

Being a dab hand at setting up experiments won't just make your investigations more reliable. You might also be asked to comment on how an experiment's been set up in the exam. So best get learning. You'll thank me for it...

Heating Substances

Heating a reaction isn't as simple as wrapping it up in a lumpy wool jumper and a stripy scarf.
There's more than one way to do it, and you need to be able to decide on the best, and the safest, method.

Bunsen Burners Have a Naked Flame

Bunsen burners are good for heating things quickly. You can easily adjust how strongly
they're heating. But you need to be careful not to use them if you're heating flammable
compounds as the flame means the substance would be at risk of catching fire.

Here's how to use a Bunsen burner...

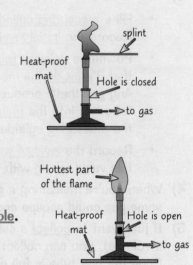

- Connect the Bunsen burner to a gas tap, and check that the
  hole is closed. Place it on a heat-proof mat.
- Light a splint and hold it over the Bunsen burner. Now, turn on
  the gas. The Bunsen burner should light with a yellow flame.
- The more open the hole is, the more strongly the Bunsen burner
  will heat your substance. Open the hole to the amount you want.
  As you open the hole more, the flame should turn more blue.
- The hottest part of the flame is just above the blue cone,
  so you should heat things here.
- If your Bunsen burner is alight but not heating anything, make sure
  you close the hole so that the flame becomes yellow and clearly visible.
- If you're heating something so that the container (e.g. a test tube)
  is in the flame, you should hold the vessel at the top, furthest away
  from the substance (and so the flame) using a pair of tongs.
- If you're heating something over the flame (e.g. an evaporating dish), you should
  put a tripod and gauze over the Bunsen burner before you light it, and place the vessel on this.

You'd use a Bunsen burner to carry out flame tests to identify metal ions in a compound (see page 95).
A sample of the compound is placed on a metal wire that you hold just above the cone of a Bunsen burner
with a blue flame. The flame should then change colour depending on what metal ion is in the sample.

The Temperature of Water Baths & Electric Heaters Can Be Set

1) A water bath is a container filled with water that can be heated to a specific temperature.

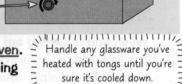

- Set the temperature on the water bath, and allow the water to heat up.
- Place the vessel containing your substance in the water bath
  using a pair of tongs. The level of the water outside the vessel
  should be just above the level of the substance inside
  the vessel. The substance will then be warmed to
  the same temperature as the water.

As the substance in the vessel is surrounded by water, the heating is very even.
Water boils at 100 °C though, so you can't use a water bath to heat something
to a higher temperature than this — the water won't get hot enough.

Handle any glassware you've heated with tongs until you're sure it's cooled down.

2) Electric heaters are often made up of a metal plate that can be heated to a certain temperature.
   The vessel containing the substance you want to heat is placed on top of the hot plate. You can heat
   substances to higher temperatures than you can in a water bath but, as the vessel is only heated from
   below, you'll usually have to stir the substance inside to make sure it's heated evenly.

A bath and an electric heater — how I spend my January nights...

You know, I used to have a chemistry teacher who'd play power ballads when the Bunsen burners were alight and
sway at the front of the class like he was at a gig. You think I made that up, but it's true.

Answers

p.12 — Chemical Equations
Q1 $2Fe + 3Cl_2 \rightarrow 2FeCl_3$ *[1 mark]*

Q2 a) water → hydrogen + oxygen *[1 mark]*

b) $2H_2O \rightarrow 2H_2 + O_2$
[1 mark for correct reactants and products, 1 mark for a correctly balanced equation]

p.13 — Chemical Equations Involving Ions
Q1 $H^+_{(aq)} + OH^-_{(aq)} \rightarrow H_2O_{(l)}$ *[1 mark]*

p.14 — Hazards and Risk
Q1 The student should wear gloves, a lab coat and goggles when handling chemical A / should only use low concentrations of chemical A *[1 mark]*. When handling chemical B, the student should take care to keep it away from naked flames *[1 mark]*.

p.15 — The History of the Atom
Q1 During the gold foil experiment, alpha particles were fired at a thin sheet of gold *[1 mark]*. The plum pudding model predicted that the alpha particles would pass straight through the sheet, or only be deflected slightly *[1 mark]*. Though most of the particles did pass straight through, a few were deflected more than expected and a small number were deflected straight back *[1 mark]*. This suggested that most of the atom is made up of empty space, with a positive nucleus in the centre *[1 mark]*.

Q2 E.g. nucleus   shells

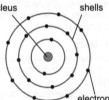

electrons

[1 mark for correct structure, 1 mark for correct labels]

p.16 — The Atom
Q1 electrons = 19 *[1 mark]*, protons = 19 *[1 mark]*, neutrons = 39 − 19 = 20 *[1 mark]*

p.17 — Isotopes and Relative Atomic Mass
Q1 $(79 \times 51) + (81 \times 49) = 7998$ *[1 mark]*
$7998 \div 100 = 79.98 = 80$ *[1 mark]*

p.18 — The Periodic Table
Q1 Potassium and sodium are both in Group 1. Potassium and calcium are in different groups. So the properties of potassium should be closer to those of sodium than calcium *[1 mark]*, because elements in the same group have similar properties *[1 mark]*.

p.19 — Electronic Configurations
Q1 2.8.3 or

[1 mark]

Q2 Group 2 *[1 mark]*
Period 4 *[1 mark]*

p.20 — Ions
Q1 Li_2O *[1 mark]*

p.21 — Ionic Bonding
Q1 Each sodium atom loses an electron to form an Na^+ ion *[1 mark]*. Each chlorine atom gains an electron to form a Cl^- ion *[1 mark]*. The oppositely charged ions are attracted to each other by electrostatic attraction *[1 mark]*.

Q2

[1 mark for arrow showing electron transferred from potassium to chlorine, 1 mark for both ions having correct electron configurations, 1 mark correct charges on ions]

p.22 — Ionic Compounds
Q1 A lot of energy is needed to break the strong attraction between the ions/the strong ionic bonds *[1 mark]*.

p.23 — Covalent Bonding
Q1 The intermolecular forces between molecules of O_2 are weak and don't need much energy to break *[1 mark]*. This gives O_2 a low boiling point (so it's a gas at room temperature) *[1 mark]*.

Q2 N_2 molecules aren't charged/don't contain any free electrons or ions *[1 mark]*.

p.24 — Giant Covalent Structures and Fullerenes
Q1 E.g. graphite can be used as a lubricant because it's soft and slippery / can be used to make electrodes because it conducts electricity *[1 mark for any correct use of graphite, 1 mark for a property of graphite that makes it suitable for the stated use.]*

p.25 — Metallic Bonding
Q1 Copper is a good electrical conductor *[1 mark]* as it contains delocalised electrons which are able to carry an electrical charge *[1 mark]*.

Q2 Sample A is likely to be the metal *[1 mark]*. Metals can conduct electricity as a solid as the metallic structure contains delocalised/free electrons that are able to carry a charge *[1 mark]*. Metals are also generally shiny *[1 mark]*.

p.26 — Conservation of Mass
Q1 The mass of the container is likely to decrease over the course of the reaction *[1 mark]* as one of the products is a gas *[1 mark]*. Since the container isn't sealed, the gas will be lost from the reaction vessel and so its mass won't be measured *[1 mark]*.

p.27 — Relative Masses and Chemical Formulas
Q1 $(2 \times 12) + (5 \times 1) + 16 + 1 = 46$ *[1 mark]*

Q2 C_2H_4Cl *[1 mark]*

p.28 — Moles
Q1 moles = mass ÷ M_r
       = 90 ÷ 18 = 5.0 moles *[1 mark]*

Q2 $3.5 \times 6.02 \times 10^{23} = 2.107 \times 10^{24}$ *[1 mark]*

Q3 moles = mass ÷ M_r
       = 81.4 ÷ 74 = 1.1 moles *[1 mark]*
$1.1 \times 6.02 \times 10^{23} = 6.622 \times 10^{23}$ *[1 mark]*
In one particle of $Ca(OH)_2$, there are 5 atoms, so in 1.1 moles, there are:
$6.622 \times 10^{23} \times 5 = 3.311 \times 10^{24}$ atoms *[1 mark]*

p.29 — More Calculations
Q1 mass = moles × M_r
= 0.200 × 119 = 23.8 moles *[1 mark]*

Q2 M_r = mass ÷ moles = 87.0 ÷ 0.500
              = 174 *[1 mark]*

Q3 $200 \text{ cm}^3 = (200 \div 1000) \text{ dm}^3 = 0.2 \text{ dm}^3$ *[1 mark]*
mass = concentration × volume
       = 55 × 0.2 = 11 g *[1 mark]*

p.30 — Calculating Empirical Formulas
Q1 mass of oxygen = 45.6 − 13.9 = 31.7 g *[1 mark]*
moles = mass ÷ M_r
moles of oxygen = 31.7 ÷ 16 = 1.98125
moles of nitrogen = 13.9 ÷ 14 = 0.99... *[1 mark]*
Divide by the smallest number (0.99...).
oxygen = 1.98125 ÷ 0.99... = 2
nitrogen = 0.99... ÷ 0.99... = 1
Ratio of O : N = 2 : 1
So empirical formula = NO_2 *[1 mark]*

p.31 — Limiting Reactants
Q1 $M_r(KBr) = 39 + 80 = 119$
$M_r(Br_2) = 80 \times 2 = 160$ *[1 mark]*
moles of KBr = mass ÷ M_r = 23.8 ÷ 119
            = 0.200 moles *[1 mark]*
From the equation, 2 moles of KBr react to produce 1 mole of Br_2. So 0.200 moles of KBr will produce (0.200 ÷ 2) = 0.100 moles of Br_2 *[1 mark]*.
So mass of Br_2 = 0.100 × 160
            = 16.0 g *[1 mark]*

p.32 — Balancing Equations using Masses
Q1 mass of element Y present
= 52.00 − 17.92 = 34.08 g *[1 mark]*
moles = mass ÷ M_r (or A_r)
moles of Fe = 17.92 ÷ 56 = 0.32 moles
moles of product = 52.00 ÷ 162.5 = 0.32 moles *[1 mark]*
moles of Y_2 = 34.08 ÷ 71 = 0.48 *[1 mark]*
So ratio of Fe : Y_2 : product
            = 0.32 : 0.48 : 0.32.
Divide them all by 0.32:
Ratio of Fe : Y_2 : product = 1 : 1.5 : 1.
Multiply by 2 to get everything to the nearest whole number:
Ratio of Fe : Y_2 : product = 2 : 3 : 2 *[1 mark]*
So balanced equation: $2Fe + 3Y_2 \rightarrow 2(product)$
To make the equation balance, the product must contain 1 atom of Fe and 3 atoms of Y.
So the balanced equation is:
$2Fe + 3Y_2 \rightarrow 2FeY_3$ *[1 mark]*

p.34 — States of Matter
Q1 gas, liquid, solid *[1 mark]*

Q2 In a gas, there's almost no force of attraction between the particles *[1 mark]*. The particles move constantly with random motion *[1 mark]*, travel in straight lines and only interact when they collide *[1 mark]*.

p.35 — Changes of State
Q1 From a gas to a liquid *[1 mark]*.

Q2 A — gas *[1 mark]*, B — solid *[1 mark]*, C — liquid *[1 mark]*.

p.36 — Purity
Q1 Under the scientific definition, a pure substance is a substance completely made up of a single element or compound *[1 mark]*. Orange juice is not chemically pure, since it is a mixture (of water, sugars and other compounds) *[1 mark]*.

Q2 No, I do not agree with Glyn. Since the sample he has is a pure chemical, it should have a sharp melting point *[1 mark]*.

p.37 — Distillation
Q1 Methanol will be collected in the first fraction *[1 mark]*, because it has the lowest boiling point of the three compounds in the mixture *[1 mark]*.

p.38 — Filtration and Crystallisation
Q1 Slowly heat the solution to evaporate off some of the water *[1 mark]*. Stop heating once some of the water has evaporated / once copper sulfate crystals start to form *[1 mark]*. Allow the solution to cool until copper sulfate crystals form *[1 mark]*. Filter the crystals out of the solution and dry them in a warm place / desiccator / drying oven *[1 mark]*.

p.39 — Chromatography
Q1 A piece of filter paper *[1 mark]*.

Q2 Chemical A will end up closer to the solvent front than B *[1 mark]*. A is more soluble in the solvent, so it will spend more time dissolved in the mobile phase, and move further up the paper *[1 mark]*.

p.40 — Interpreting Chromatograms
Q1 R_f of Y = distance travelled by Y ÷ distance travelled by solvent front
= 3.6 cm ÷ 6.0 cm *[1 mark]* = 0.60 *[1 mark]*

p.41 — Water Treatment

Q1 The water is first filtered through a wire mesh to filter out large objects and through gravel and sand to filter out smaller solid objects *[1 mark]*. Then, a sedimentation process is used. This involves adding aluminium sulfate / iron sulfate to the water, causing fine particles to clump together and settle at the bottom *[1 mark]*. Finally, chlorine gas is bubbled through the water to kill harmful bacteria *[1 mark]*.

Q2 Tap water could contain other ions that might interfere with the reaction *[1 mark]*. He should use deionised water instead *[1 mark]*.

p.43 — Acids and Bases

Q1 acidic *[1 mark]*

p.44 — Strong and Weak Acids

Q1 A strong acid ionises/dissociates almost completely in water *[1 mark]*. A weak acid only ionises/dissociates a small amount in water *[1 mark]*.

Q2 It increased *[1 mark]* by a factor of 1000 *[1 mark]*.

p.45 — Reactions of Acids

Q1 $2HCl + CaCO_3 \rightarrow CaCl_2 + H_2O + CO_2$
[1 mark for correct reactants and products, 1 mark for a correctly balanced equation]

p.46 — Making Insoluble Salts

Q1 a) soluble *[1 mark]*

b) insoluble *[1 mark]*

c) insoluble *[1 mark]*

d) soluble *[1 mark]*

Q2 E.g. barium nitrate/barium chloride and copper sulfate *[1 mark for any soluble barium salt and 1 mark for any soluble sulfate]*

p.47 — Making Soluble Salts

Q1 E.g. add the base/iron oxide to warmed acid *[1 mark]*. Keep on adding base until all the acid has been neutralised. At this point, no more base will react and it will sink to the bottom of the flask *[1 mark]*. Filter out the excess solid using filter paper *[1 mark]*. Evaporate off some of the water from the salt solution and leave it until salt crystals form *[1 mark]*. Filter off the crystals and leave them to dry *[1 mark]*.

p.48 — Electrolysis

Q1 anode *[1 mark]*

p.49 — Predicting Products of Electrolysis

Q1 $2Br^- \rightarrow Br_2 + 2e^-$ *[1 mark for correct formulas, 1 mark for balancing]*

p.50 — Electrolysis of Copper Sulfate

Q1 The anode is a big lump of impure copper *[1 mark]* and the cathode is a thin piece of pure copper *[1 mark]*. During the electrolysis, the electrical supply pulls electrons off copper atoms at the impure copper anode so they dissolve and form copper ions *[1 mark]*. These copper ions migrate to the cathode where they accept electrons to reform copper atoms, and coat the cathode with a pure layer of copper *[1 mark]*.

p.52 — The Reactivity Series

Q1 H / hydrogen *[1 mark]*

Q2 Calcium is more easily oxidised as it's higher up the reactivity series/it's more reactive *[1 mark]*.

p.53 — Reactivity of Metals

Q1 a) Metal B, Metal C, Metal A *[1 mark]*

b) Metal A is copper. Metal B is magnesium. Metal C is zinc *[1 mark for all three correct]*.

p.54 — Displacement Reactions

Q1 Silver would not displace iron from iron chloride solution, because it's lower down than iron in the reactivity series/less reactive than iron *[1 mark]*.

Q2 Lithium would displace zinc from zinc sulfate solution, as it's higher than zinc in the reactivity series/it's more reactive than zinc *[1 mark]*.

p.55 — Extracting Metals Using Carbon

Q1 Tin is less reactive than carbon *[1 mark]* so you could extract tin from its ore by reducing it with carbon *[1 mark]*.

Q2 E.g. $2ZnO + C \rightarrow 2Zn + CO_2$
[1 mark for correct reactants and products, 1 mark for balanced equation]

p.56 — Other Methods of Extracting Metals

Q1 Aluminium would be more expensive to extract than iron *[1 mark]* as aluminium is more reactive than carbon, so has to be extracted using electrolysis, whereas iron can be extracted by reduction with carbon *[1 mark]*. Extracting metals using electrolysis is much more expensive than using reduction with carbon as it requires high temperatures to melt the metal ore which is expensive/there are costs associated with using electricity, whereas reduction using carbon is much cheaper *[1 mark]*.

p.57 — Recycling

Q1 E.g. Metals are non-renewable, so recycling metals is important to conserve finite resources of the metal *[1 mark]*. Also, non-recycled material has to be disposed of in landfill sites, which take up space and can pollute the surroundings *[1 mark]*.

p.58 — Life Cycle Assessments

Q1 Any four from, e.g. the energy required to extract the raw materials / whether the raw materials are renewable or not / whether other harmful emissions (e.g. CO/HCl) are produced / whether the waste products are harmful or not / how environmentally friendly the cars are to dispose of *[1 mark for each]*.

p.59 — Dynamic Equilibrium

Q1 A reversible reaction is one where the products can react with each other to produce the reactants *[1 mark]*.

Q2 Dynamic equilibrium occurs when the forward and backward reactions in a reversible reaction occur at the same time *[1 mark]* and at the same rate *[1 mark]*, so there is no change in concentration of the reactants or the products *[1 mark]*.

p.60 — Le Chatelier's Principle

Q1 The position of equilibrium will shift to the right (towards the products) *[1 mark]*. The forward reaction is endothermic, so when the temperature is increased the equilibrium position will move to the right to absorb the excess heat *[1 mark]*.

Q2 Decreasing the pressure would shift the equilibrium position to the left (towards the reactants) *[1 mark]* as there are more moles of gas on the reactant side than on the product side *[1 mark]*. So the yield of SO_3 would decrease *[1 mark]*.

p.62 — Transition Metals

Q1 E.g. Haber process and iron / Contact process and vanadium pentoxide/V_2O_5 *[1 mark for any industrial process and matching catalyst]*.

Q2 Palladium, as in general transition metals have higher densities than Group 1 metals *[1 mark]*.

p.63 — Alloys

Q1 Any one from, e.g. girders / bridges / engine parts / cutlery / saucepans / drill bits / cars *[1 mark]*.

Q2 Pure aluminium is not strong enough for making aeroplanes so it's alloyed with small amounts of other metals to make it stronger *[1 mark]*.

p.64 — Corrosion

Q1 Magnesium is more reactive than iron *[1 mark]*, so will lose electrons/be oxidised/react with water and oxygen in preference to iron *[1 mark]*.

p.65 — Titrations

Q1 moles of HCl = $0.50 \times (27 \div 1000)$
= 0.0135 moles
According to the equation, 1 mole of HCl reacts with 1 mole of NaOH, so 0.0135 moles of HCl must react with 0.0135 moles of NaOH.
concentration of NaOH = moles ÷ volume
= $0.0135 \div (15 \div 1000)$ = 0.90 mol dm^{-3}
[4 marks for correct answer, otherwise 1 mark for correct moles of HCl, 1 mark for correct moles of NaOH, 1 mark for correct equation to work out concentration of NaOH]

p.66 — Percentage Yield

Q1 $M_r(Ag_2O) = (2 \times 108) + 16 = 232$
$A_r(Ag) = 108$
Moles Ag_2O = 3.48 ÷ 232 = 0.015 mol
The equation tells you that 2 moles of Ag_2O form 4 moles of Ag, so 0.015 moles of Ag_2O produce $(0.015 \div 2) \times 4$ = 0.030 moles of Ag.
Mass of 0.030 moles of Ag = 0.030×108
= 3.24 g
So % yield = $(1.62 \div 3.24) \times 100$ = 50%
[4 marks for the correct answer, otherwise 1 mark for the correct moles of Ag, 1 mark for theoretical yield of Ag, 1 mark for correct use of percentage yield equation]

p.67 — Atom Economy

Q1 M_r of all products = $M_r(CO_2) + [2 \times M_r(H_2)]$
= $[12 + (2 \times 16)] + [2 \times (2 \times 1)]$
= 44 + 4 = 48
M_r of desired product = $2 \times M_r(H_2)$
= $2 \times (2 \times 1)$ = 4
Atom economy = $(4 \div 48) \times 100$ = 8.3%
[4 marks for the correct answer, otherwise 1 mark for the correct M_r of products and reactants, 1 mark for dividing M_r of desired products by M_r of all products, 1 mark for multiplication of 100]

Q2 Any two from, e.g. to minimise the resources used / to reduce the waste created / to reduce costs of raw materials / to reduce costs of cleaning up waste *[1 mark for each reason]*.

p.68 — The Haber Process

Q1 The yield of ammonia would increase *[1 mark]*. A higher pressure would favour the forward reaction/push the position of equilibrium over to the right as there are fewer moles of gas in the products *[1 mark]*.

p.69 —Fertilisers

Q1 Fertilisers replace / provide the essential elements that a plant needs to grow *[1 mark]*.

Q2 Set up titration apparatus by filling a burette with sulfuric acid solution, and clamping it over a conical flask containing ammonia solution *[1 mark]*. Add a few drops of methyl orange indicator *[1 mark]*. Then, slowly add the sulfuric acid until the solution changes from yellow to red *[1 mark]*. Repeat this experiment using identical quantities of sulfuric acid and ammonia solution, but with no indicator *[1 mark]*. Then, gently evaporate the solution until only a little bit is left and leave to allow ammonia sulfate crystals to form *[1 mark]*. Filter the crystals out of the solution and leave to dry *[1 mark]*.

p.70 — Calculations with Gases

Q1 moles = mass ÷ A_r
moles of Ar = 2.4 ÷ 40 = 0.060 mol
molar volume = volume ÷ moles
= 1.32 ÷ 0.060
= 22 dm^3 mol^{-1}
[2 marks for correct answer, otherwise 1 mark for correct moles of Ar]

Q2 moles = mass ÷ M_r
moles of CH_4 = 36 ÷ 16 = 2.25 moles
volume = moles × 24 = 2.25 × 24
= 54 dm^3
[2 marks for correct answer, otherwise 1 mark for correct moles of CH_4]

p.71 — Fuel Cells

Q1 $2H_2 + O_2 \rightarrow 2H_2O$ *[1 mark]*

Q2 Advantage: any one from, e.g. they don't generate pollutants / they're efficient *[1 mark]*. Disadvantage: any one from, e.g. hydrogen gas takes up lots of space to store / hydrogen is explosive, so it's difficult to store safely / production of hydrogen uses electricity, which is often made by burning fossil fuels *[1 mark]*.

p.73 — Group 1 — Alkali Metals

Q1 The lithium should move around the surface of the water, fizzing vigorously, then dissolve *[1 mark]*.

Q2 $2K + 2H_2O \rightarrow 2KOH + H_2$ *[1 mark for correct products and reactants and 1 mark for correct balancing]*

Answers

p.74 — Group 7 — Halogens

Q1 $2Na + Br_2 \rightarrow 2NaBr$ *[1 mark for correct products and reactants and 1 mark for correct balancing]*

p.75 — Halogen Displacement Reactions

Q1 He should add a few drops of the solution to a bromine salt solution (e.g. potassium bromide) *[1 mark]*. If the solution turns orange, the halogen solution contains chlorine. If there is no reaction, the halogen solution contains bromine *[1 mark]*.

p.76 — Group 0 — Noble Gases

Q1 Any melting point between −150 °C and 80 °C *[1 mark]*.

p.77 — Reaction Rates

Q1 E.g. put a conical flask on a mass balance and add your reactants *[1 mark]*. As gas is produced from the reaction, measure how quickly the reading on the balance drops until the balance stops changing *[1 mark]*. Plot the results in a graph of change in mass against time *[1 mark]*.

Q2 E.g. the result is subjective *[1 mark]*.

p.78 — Rate Experiments Involving Gases

Q1 E.g. place a measured volume of hydrochloric acid of a known concentration in a conical flask. Add a known mass of calcium carbonate in the form of marble chips *[1 mark]*. Immediately add a gas syringe. Take readings of the volume of gas produced at regular time intervals *[1 mark]*. Repeat the experiment with the same volume and concentration of acid and the same mass of calcium carbonate but increase the surface area of magnesium by crunching the marble up. Repeat again with the same mass of powdered chalk *[1 mark]*.

p.79 — Rate Experiments Involving Precipitation

Q1 The time taken would decrease *[1 mark]*.

p.80 — Calculating Rates

Q1 E.g.

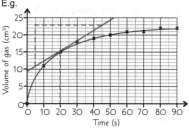

[1 mark]

Change in y = 23 − 11 = 12
Change in x = 45 − 5 = 40
Gradient = 12 ÷ 40 = 0.30 cm^3 s^{-1}
[1 mark for a rate between 0.25 cm³ s⁻¹ and 0.40 cm³ s⁻¹]

p.81 — Collision Theory

Q1 The energy transferred during a collision (particles must collide with enough energy for the collision to be successful) *[1 mark]* and the collision frequency *[1 mark]*.

Q2 Breaking a solid into smaller pieces will increase the surface area to volume ratio *[1 mark]*. This means that particles of the other reactant will have more area to work on *[1 mark]*. This increases the frequency of collisions and speeds up the rate of reaction *[1 mark]*.

p.82 — Catalysts

Q1 A catalyst is a substance which increases the rate of reaction *[1 mark]*, without being chemically changed or used up *[1 mark]*.

Q2 The manganese dioxide is not chemically changed or used up so only a tiny amount is needed to catalyse a large quantity of reactant *[1 mark]*.

Q3 Enzymes are biological catalysts *[1 mark]*. They speed up chemical reactions inside living cells *[1 mark]*.

p.83 — Endothermic and Exothermic Reactions

Q1 The products are at a higher energy than the reactants so the reaction must be endothermic *[1 mark]*. This means the reaction mixture must have decreased in temperature *[1 mark]*.

p.84 — Measuring Temperature Changes

Q1 They help to insulate the reaction mixture, limiting the energy transferred to or from the surroundings and by evaporation *[1 mark]*.

p.85 — Bond Energies

Q1 Energy required to break original bonds:
$(1 \times N{\equiv}N) + (3 \times H{-}H)$
= 941 + (3 × 436) = 941 + 1308
= 2249 kJ mol^{-1} *[1 mark]*
Energy released by forming new bonds:
$(6 \times N{-}H)$
= 6 × 391 = 2346 kJ mol^{-1} *[1 mark]*
Overall energy change:
= 2249 − 2346 = −97 kJ mol^{-1} *[1 mark]*

p.87 — Fractional Distillation

Q1 Crude oil is heated until most of it turns into a gas *[1 mark]*. The gases enter a fractionating column and the liquid part/bitumen is drained off at the bottom *[1 mark]*. There's a temperature gradient in the column — the column is hot at the bottom and cooler at the top *[1 mark]*. The longer hydrocarbons with high boiling points turn back into liquids and drain out lower down the column *[1 mark]*. Shorter hydrocarbons have lower boiling points so turn into liquids and are drained off higher up the column *[1 mark]*.

p.88 — Hydrocarbons

Q1 $C_9H_{20} + 14O_2 \rightarrow 9CO_2 + 10H_2O$
[1 mark for correct formulas, 1 mark for balancing]

p.89 — Pollutants

Q1 Carbon monoxide *[1 mark]* and soot *[1 mark]*.

p.90 — Cracking

Q1 Cracking involves breaking strong covalent bonds within alkane molecules *[1 mark]*.

Q2 $C_{12}H_{26}$ *[1 mark]*

p.91 — The Atmosphere

Q1 A lot of the early CO_2 dissolved into the oceans *[1 mark]*. Green plants evolved and removed CO_2 from the atmosphere through photosynthesis *[1 mark]*. Much of the CO_2 got locked up in fossil fuels and sedimentary rocks *[1 mark]*.

p.92 — The Greenhouse Effect

Q1 A gas in the atmosphere that can absorb and reflect heat radiation *[1 mark]*.

Q2 Any two from, e.g. more people means more CO_2 given out from respiration / more energy needed for day to day living e.g. lighting, transport and cooking — this energy comes mainly from burning fossil fuels which releases CO_2 / space made for houses and farming through deforestation means that less CO_2 is taken out of the atmosphere by photosynthesis *[1 mark for each correct answer]*.

p.93 — Climate Change

Q1 Global warming is a type of climate change where the Earth's average temperature has increased *[1 mark]*. Increased human activity is believed to have caused increased levels of greenhouse gases in our atmosphere which has resulted in an enhanced greenhouse effect *[1 mark]*.

Q2 Any two from, e.g. walk or cycle instead of drive / turn your central heating down / use more renewable energy *[1 mark for each correct answer]*.

p.95 — Tests for Cations

Q1 The compound contains potassium/K^+ ions *[1 mark]*.

Q2 The solution contains iron(III)/Fe^{3+} ions *[1 mark]*.

p.96 — Tests for Anions

Q1 The solution contains iodide ions *[1 mark]*.

p.97 — Flame Photometry

Q1 Any two from, e.g.: using machines is very sensitive / using machines is very fast / using machines is very accurate / flame photometry can be used to identify the metal ions in mixtures *[1 mark for each correct advantage]*.

p.98 — Alkanes and Alkenes

Q1

H—C—C=C with H atoms *[1 mark]*

p.99 — Addition Polymers

Q1

polymer structure with CH₃ group *[1 mark]*

p.100 — Condensation Polymers

Q1 A dicarboxylic acid monomer and a diol monomer *[1 mark]*.

Q2 E.g. by the formation of an ester link *[1 mark]*.

p.101 — Disposing of Polymers

Q1 E.g. if not controlled, toxic gases can be released from burning plastics / carbon dioxide is released when plastics are burned which contributes to the greenhouse effect *[1 mark for each correct disadvantage, up to a maximum of 2 marks]*.

Q2 Polymers are made from crude oil *[1 mark]*. Crude oil is a finite resource *[1 mark]* so the more of it we use up, the more expensive it will become and this will increase the price of polymer products *[1 mark]*.

p.102 — Alcohols and Carboxylic Acids

Q1 methanol *[1 mark]*

Q2 propanol *[1 mark]*

p.103 — Production of Ethanol

Q1 Carbohydrate/sugars *[1 mark]*

Q2 Fermentation is fastest between 30 °C and 40 °C *[1 mark]*. Temperatures higher than this denature the enzyme in the yeast *[1 mark]*.

Q3 Fractional distillation produces a solution of ethanol with a concentration above 20% from the fermentation mixture *[1 mark]*.

p.104 — Combustion of Alcohols

Q1 Alcohol Y *[1 mark]*

p.105 — Nanoparticles

Q1 Any three from, e.g.: catalysts / lubricant coatings / tiny electrical circuits / antibacterial materials / sun creams / stronger plastics *[1 mark for each correct use]*.

p.106 — Types of Materials

Q1 Any two from, e.g.: fibreglass / concrete / carbon fibre *[1 mark for each correct material]*.

p.107 — Materials and their Uses

Q1 E.g. poly(propene) would be the best choice *[1 mark]*. The flask should be a poor thermal conductor, so that the contents of the flask stay warm, so copper and steel are poor choices *[1 mark]*. Carbon fibre is very expensive, and since the flask does not need to be especially strong, poly(propene) is a better choice *[1 mark]*.

Index

Index

The Periodic Table

Key:

Relative atomic mass →	1
	H
	Hydrogen
Atomic number →	1

Periods	Group 1	Group 2												Group 3	Group 4	Group 5	Group 6	Group 7	Group 0
1	1 **H** Hydrogen 1																		4 **He** Helium 2
2	7 **Li** Lithium 3	9 **Be** Beryllium 4												11 **B** Boron 5	12 **C** Carbon 6	14 **N** Nitrogen 7	16 **O** Oxygen 8	19 **F** Fluorine 9	20 **Ne** Neon 10
3	23 **Na** Sodium 11	24 **Mg** Magnesium 12												27 **Al** Aluminium 13	28 **Si** Silicon 14	31 **P** Phosphorus 15	32 **S** Sulfur 16	35.5 **Cl** Chlorine 17	40 **Ar** Argon 18
4	39 **K** Potassium 19	40 **Ca** Calcium 20	45 **Sc** Scandium 21	48 **Ti** Titanium 22	51 **V** Vanadium 23	52 **Cr** Chromium 24	55 **Mn** Manganese 25	56 **Fe** Iron 26	59 **Co** Cobalt 27	59 **Ni** Nickel 28	63.5 **Cu** Copper 29	65 **Zn** Zinc 30		70 **Ga** Gallium 31	73 **Ge** Germanium 32	75 **As** Arsenic 33	79 **Se** Selenium 34	80 **Br** Bromine 35	84 **Kr** Krypton 36
5	85 **Rb** Rubidium 37	88 **Sr** Strontium 38	89 **Y** Yttrium 39	91 **Zr** Zirconium 40	93 **Nb** Niobium 41	96 **Mo** Molybdenum 42	98 **Tc** Technetium 43	101 **Ru** Ruthenium 44	103 **Rh** Rhodium 45	106 **Pd** Palladium 46	108 **Ag** Silver 47	112 **Cd** Cadmium 48		115 **In** Indium 49	119 **Sn** Tin 50	122 **Sb** Antimony 51	128 **Te** Tellurium 52	127 **I** Iodine 53	131 **Xe** Xenon 54
6	133 **Cs** Caesium 55	137 **Ba** Barium 56	139 **La** Lanthanum 57	178 **Hf** Hafnium 72	181 **Ta** Tantalum 73	184 **W** Tungsten 74	186 **Re** Rhenium 75	190 **Os** Osmium 76	192 **Ir** Iridium 77	195 **Pt** Platinum 78	197 **Au** Gold 79	201 **Hg** Mercury 80		204 **Tl** Thallium 81	207 **Pb** Lead 82	209 **Bi** Bismuth 83	209 **Po** Polonium 84	210 **At** Astatine 85	222 **Rn** Radon 86
7	223 **Fr** Francium 87	226 **Ra** Radium 88	227 **Ac** Actinium 89	261 **Rf** Rutherfordium 104	262 **Db** Dubnium 105	266 **Sg** Seaborgium 106	264 **Bh** Bohrium 107	277 **Hs** Hassium 108	268 **Mt** Meitnerium 109	271 **Ds** Darmstadtium 110	272 **Rg** Roentgenium 111								